THE GREAT BIG BOREDOM BASHING ACTIVITY BOOK

This edition published in 2011 by Arcturus Publishing Limited
26/27 Bickels Yard, 151–153 Bermondsey Street,
London SE1 3HA

ISBN: 978-1-84193-696-3
CH000633EN

Illustrations, Activities & Page Layout by CREATIVE QUOTIENT

Printed in Singapore

Ready for hours of boredom bashing fun?
Then grab a pencil and get going!

GO SLOW!

You'll need to have your wits about you at this traffic crossing to find all the objects given below that are hidden in this picture.

- Apple
- Ball
- Book
- Bull's eye
- Chess piece
- Kite
- Periscope
- Ruler
- Tap
- Teddy bear

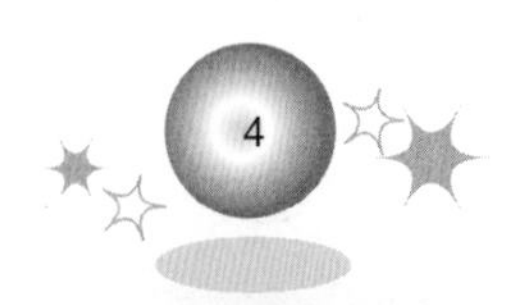

DOWN AND ACROSS!

How good are you at reading pictures? You had better be good!
Use the visual hints to correctly fill in the words in this picture crossword.

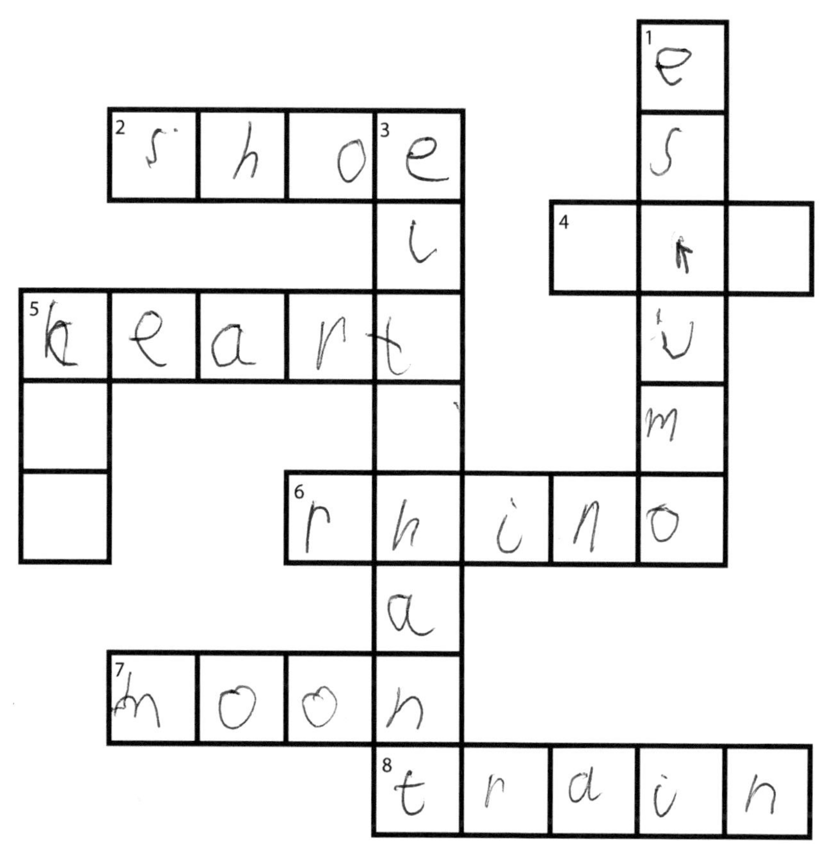

Across

②

④

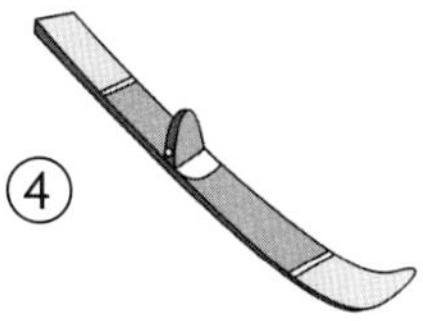

⑤

⑥

⑦

⑧

Down

①

③

⑤

DINOSAUR DUO!

There are two identical dinosaurs amongst this group.
Look carefully at all images and draw a circle around the two that are exactly the same.

IN-BETWEEN!

The first and last letters of some five-letter words are given below. How many can you think of? To start you off, the first word could be FRUIT.

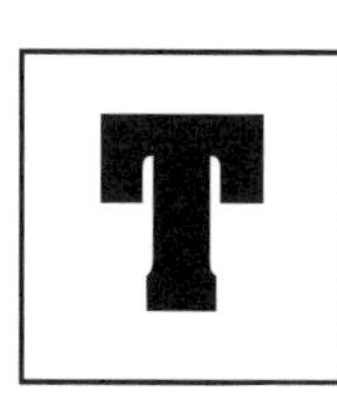

F _ _ _ T

F _ _ _ T

F _ _ _ T

F _ _ _ T

F _ _ _ T

F _ _ _ T

F _ _ _ T

F _ _ _ T

F _ _ _ T

F _ _ _ T

F _ _ _ T

F _ _ _ T

Good: 1 – 2

V. Good: 3 – 8

Excellent: 9 – 12

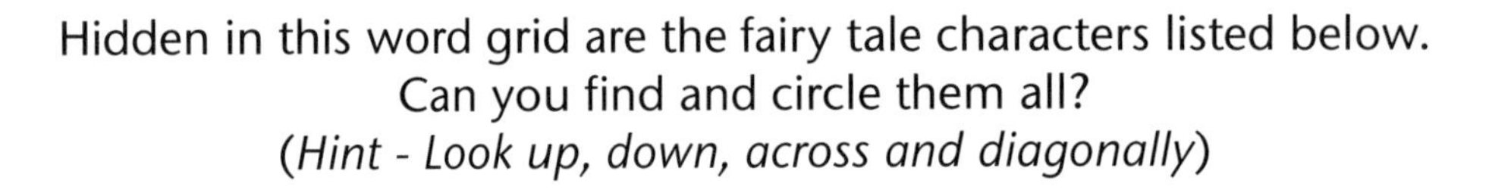

Hidden in this word grid are the fairy tale characters listed below.
Can you find and circle them all?
(Hint - Look up, down, across and diagonally)

D	T	I	P	N	B	H	L	I	H	Y	J	D	G	H
I	S	H	K	I	N	L	U	E	J	C	D	C	A	W
A	N	P	U	P	U	R	U	Q	Z	D	H	N	Z	Z
M	O	P	T	M	I	A	N	I	B	N	S	V	C	R
R	W	C	P	N	B	K	V	W	Q	E	U	O	F	N
E	W	N	K	M	F	E	R	Y	L	B	C	P	B	A
M	H	T	D	R	J	E	L	A	A	X	F	A	A	P
E	I	D	O	O	H	G	N	I	D	I	R	D	E	R
L	T	L	S	Z	S	D	T	C	N	E	E	F	H	E
T	E	Z	P	R	G	U	X	Z	O	A	N	W	A	T
T	W	N	L	R	O	O	W	M	T	J	N	R	Z	E
I	M	W	E	S	T	V	F	O	T	L	Q	W	B	P
L	Y	T	C	I	N	D	E	R	E	L	L	A	V	E
Z	E	D	R	A	E	B	E	U	L	B	F	E	Z	I
L	E	K	Z	I	F	J	I	B	G	Y	V	E	F	C

BLUE BEARD
LITTLE MERMAID
RED RIDING HOOD

CINDERELLA
PETER PAN
SNOW WHITE

HANSEL AND GRETEL
RAPUNZEL
THUMBELINA

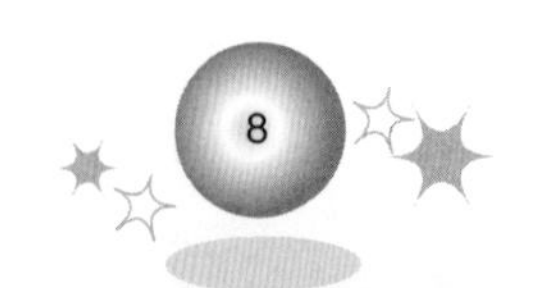

A TABLE TO REMEMBER!

Can you remember all that you see? Well, let's find out! Study this picture carefully and then turn the page to answer some questions. No peeking back at this page!

QUESTIONS

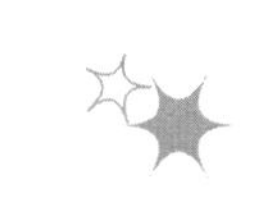

1. What is the time showing on the table clock?
2. How many pencils are there?
3. Is there a dictionary among the books?
4. Is the computer on or off?
5. What is lying on the computer?
6. What is hanging on the back of the chair?
7. Is there a book shelf?
8. Are there flowers in the vase?
9. Is it winter or spring?
10. Is there a snail on the window sill?

SEVEN STEPS!

Starting from the top, move down each step adding one letter as you go then rearrange all the letters around the 'A' to make a new word every time.

GUESS!

Here's a mystery picture for you to identify.
Just draw what you see in each of the numbered boxes below into the blank boxes which have the same number on the opposite page.

1	2	3
4	5	6
7	8	9

LETTER LEADS!

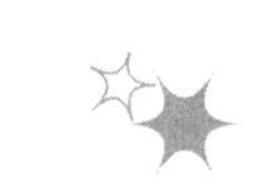

These letters make a word when they are put in the right order. Track each letter along its path and then write it in its correct place to find out what the word is.

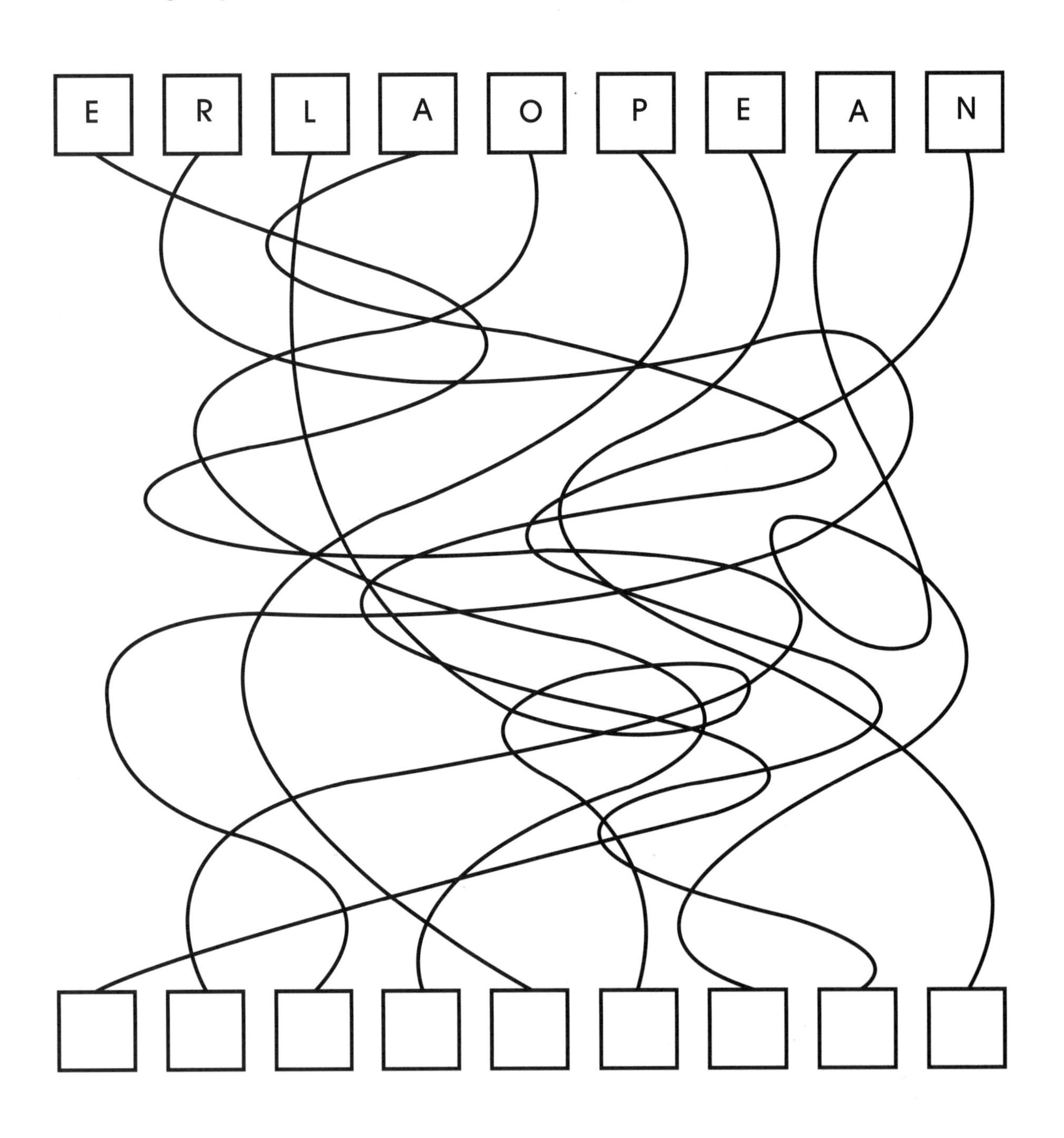

PARALLEL OR NOT?

Are your eyes playing tricks? Look sharp and decide if these lines are parallel or not!

MUM AND ME!

What fun it is to go food shopping with mum!
Can you help us find all the items on our list hidden in this picture?

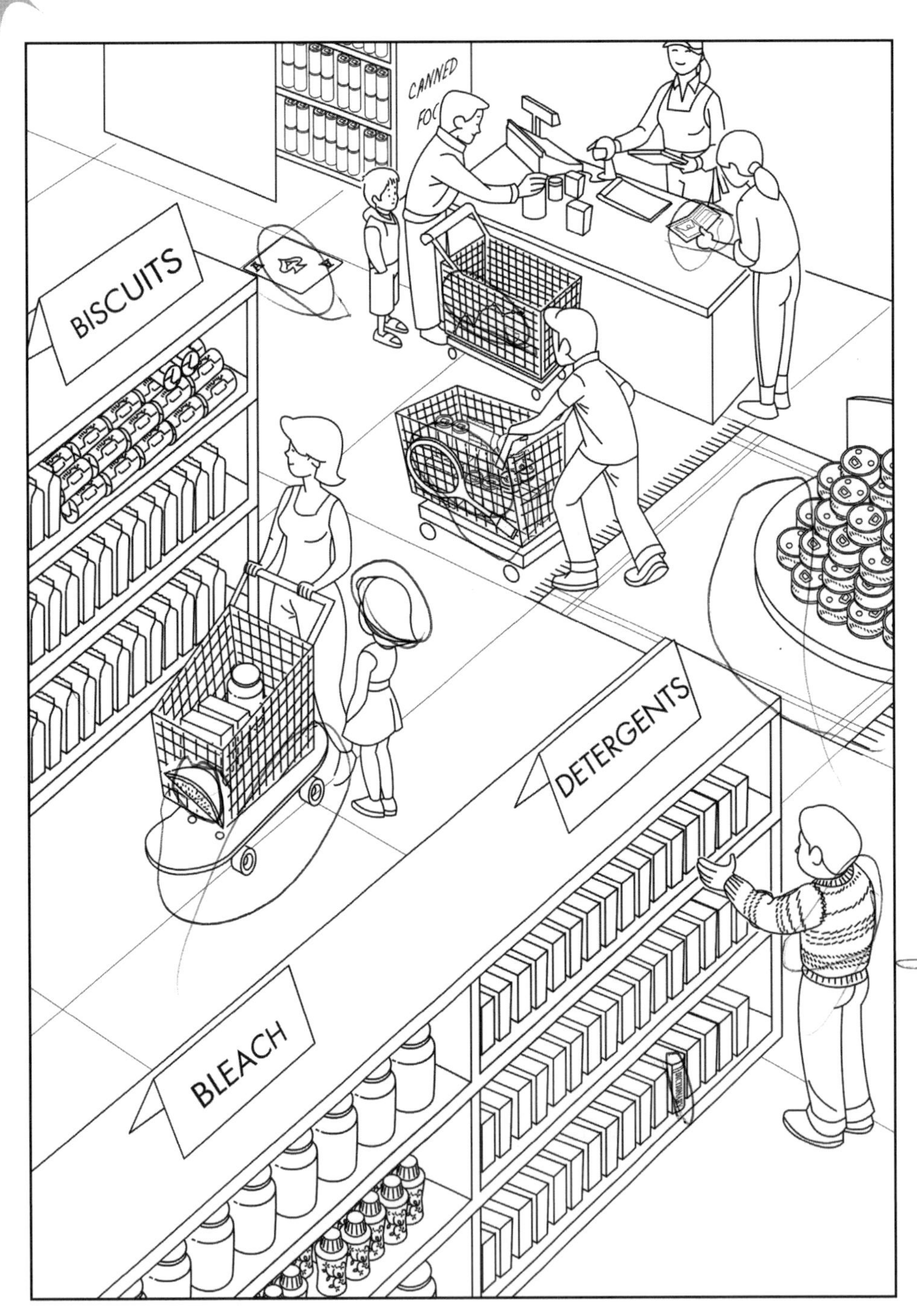

Ace of spades
Conch shell
Dictionary
Graph
Skateboard
Sweater
Tennis racquet
Towel
Wallet
Watermelon slice

CRISS-CROSS!

How good are you at reading pictures? You had better be good!
Use the visual hints to correctly fill in the words in this picture crossword.

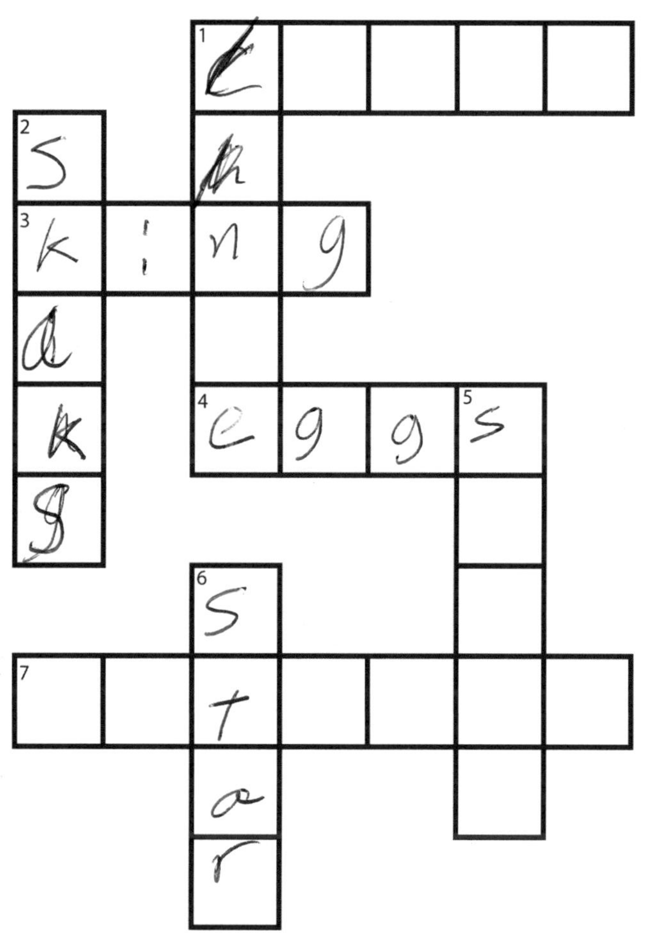

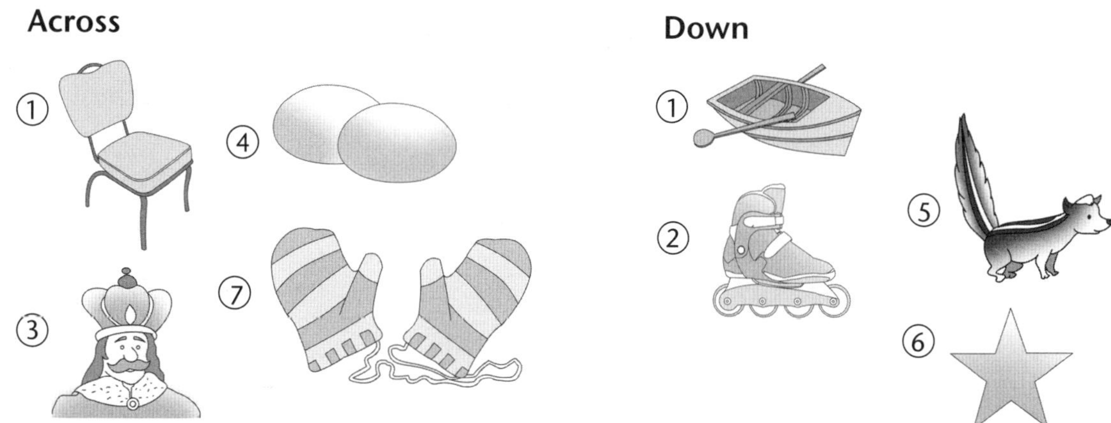

DOUBLE SCOOPS!

There are two identical ice-creams in this group.
Look carefully at the pictures and draw a circle around the two that are exactly the same.

MIDDLE MUDDLE!

The first and last letters of some five letter words are given below.
How many can you think of? To start you off, the first word could be HARSH.

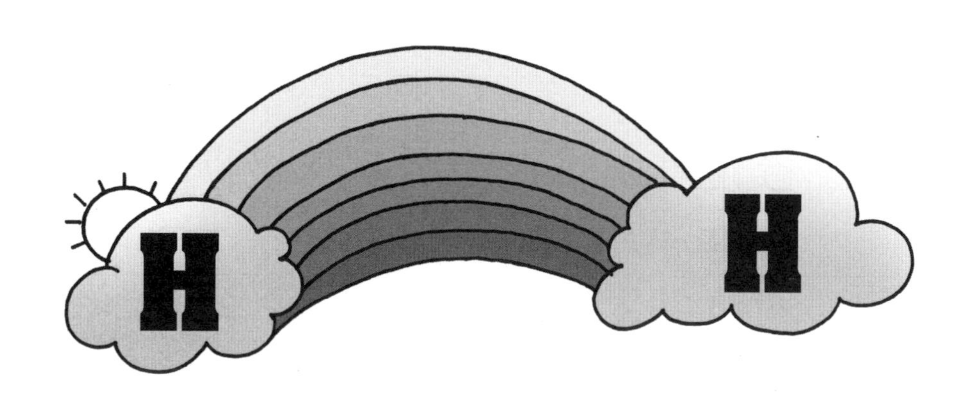

H _ _ _ H

H _ _ _ H

H _ _ _ H

H _ _ _ H

H _ _ _ H

☺	Good:	1 – 2
☺	V. Good:	3
☺	Excellent:	4 – 5

ANIMAL KINGDOM!

It's a jungle in here! Study the list of animals, then look up, down, across and diagonally in the word grid and circle all that you find.

E	R	O	S	L	S	D	U	S	B	Q	R	B	G	Z
H	J	Z	I	W	O	L	X	Z	K	L	Y	P	O	M
W	B	O	O	M	R	H	Y	V	W	L	S	E	T	H
B	N	O	R	A	E	B	X	P	D	S	M	N	B	H
R	L	A	E	X	C	I	P	B	W	D	A	P	X	V
V	Z	G	P	O	O	F	D	I	X	H	W	Z	X	G
O	O	Y	L	P	N	H	W	K	P	Q	O	K	B	S
D	R	K	N	C	I	G	A	E	I	F	C	T	I	C
V	B	E	D	Z	H	N	L	E	O	P	E	V	V	K
H	H	I	E	H	R	E	H	Y	U	T	Z	K	N	O
O	B	E	N	D	Z	V	T	H	J	W	I	M	Q	Z
R	K	U	A	V	Y	H	Q	C	D	Z	D	G	G	Z
S	X	D	C	E	C	N	M	U	K	J	R	C	E	B
E	Y	P	T	C	W	M	O	N	K	E	Y	V	F	R
H	S	G	J	D	U	N	H	G	B	G	Q	W	N	B

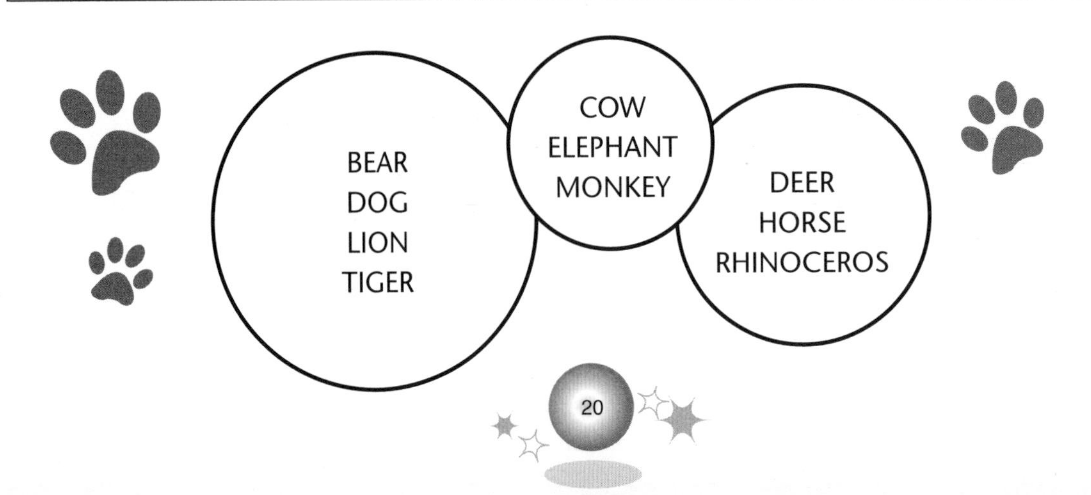

HANDBAG HANDOUTS!

Can you remember all that you see? Well, let's find out! Study this picture carefully and then turn the page to answer some questions. No peeking back at this page though!

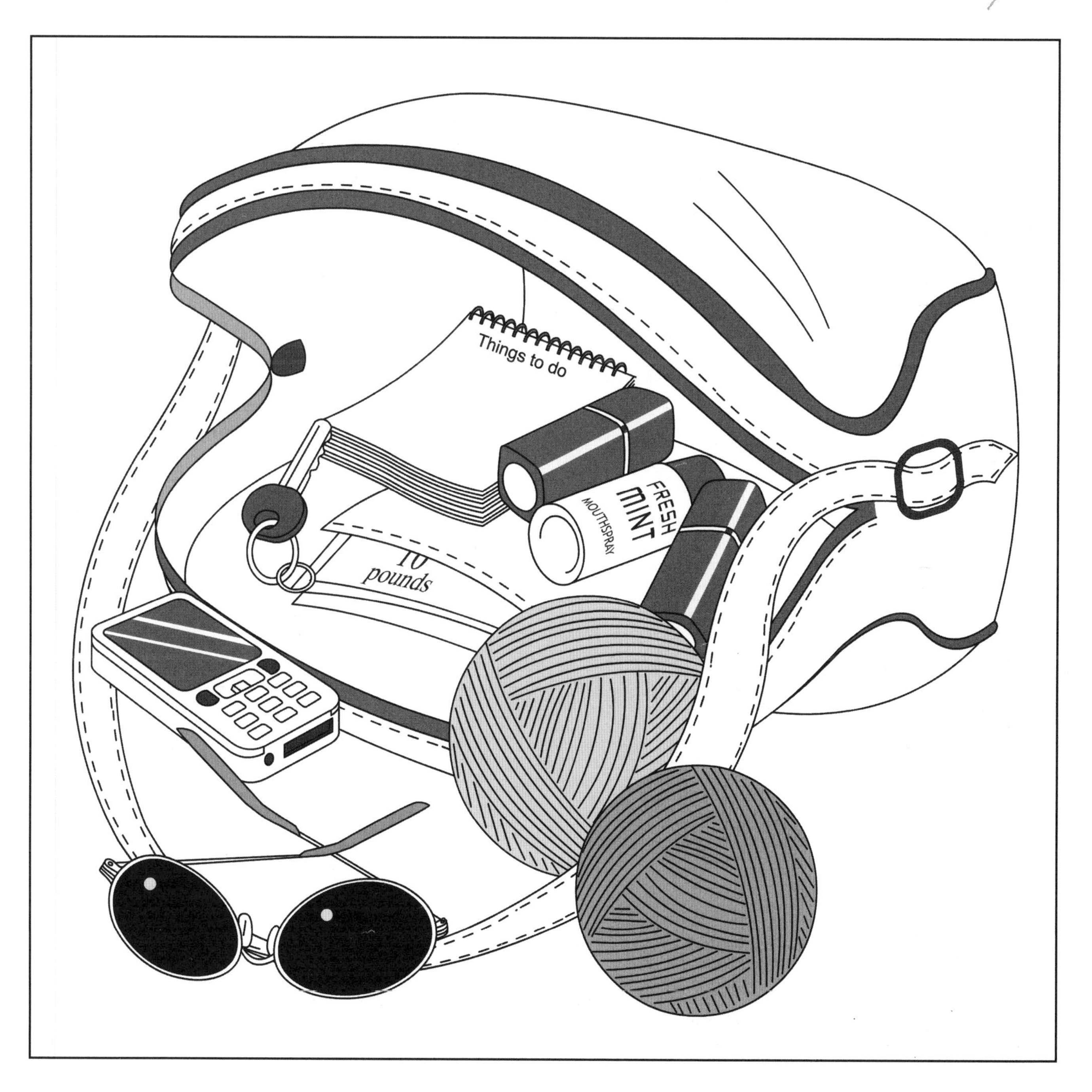

QUESTIONS

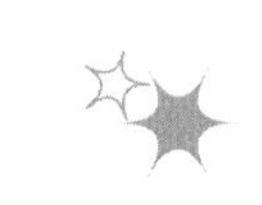

1. Are there any keys? yes
2. How many lipsticks are there? 2
3. Does the handbag have a long or a short strap? short
4. Is there a yo-yo in there? no
5. What is written on the note paper? thing to do
6. What is the denomination of the currency note? pound
7. What is the shape of the sunglasses – oval or rectangle? oval
8. Is the cell phone ringing? NO
9. What flavour is the mouth spray? mint
10. Are there any needles in the knitting wool? no

WONDER WORDS!

Starting from the top, move down each step adding one letter as you go then rearrange all the letters around the 'O' to make a new word every time.

GUESSING GRID!

Here's a mystery picture for you to identify.
Just draw what you see in each of the numbered boxes below into the blank boxes which have the same number on the opposite page.

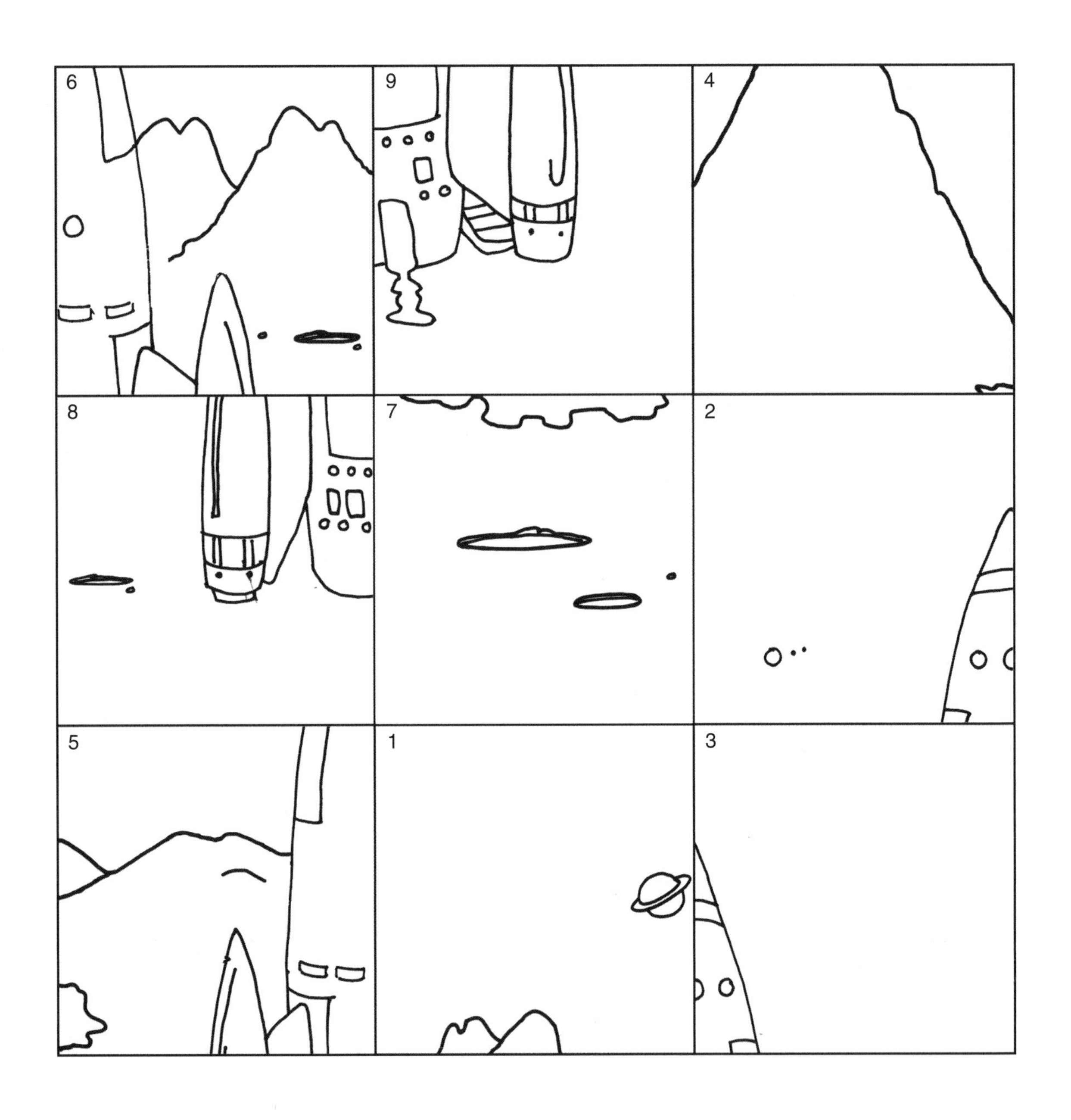

1	2	3
4	5	6
7	8	9

LOST LETTERS!

These letters make a word when they are put in the right order. Track each letter along its path and then write it in its correct place to find out what the word is.

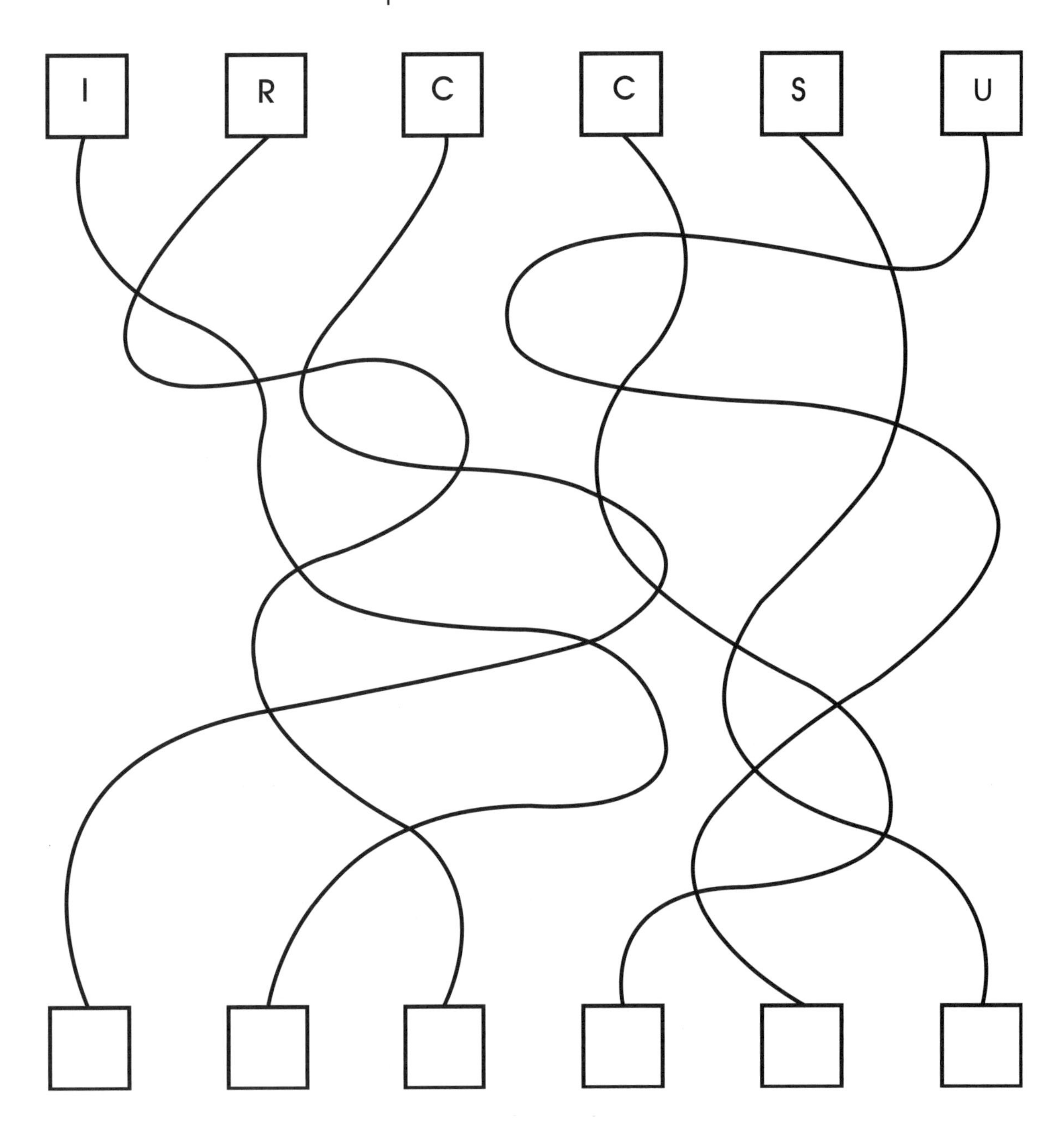

GENDER BENDER!

Whose picture can you see in this image?
Is it a beautiful young lady or a man with a moustache?

TIDY TOWN!

This is a really tidy street, isn't it? However, some things have been left lying about. Look at the list below and then find them all.

Barcode

Bench

Coins

Dentures

Frankenstein

Hand mirror

Kennel

Plaster

Robot

Tortoise

TAKE YOUR PIX!

How good are you at reading pictures? You had better be good!
Use the visual hints to correctly fill in the words in this picture crossword.

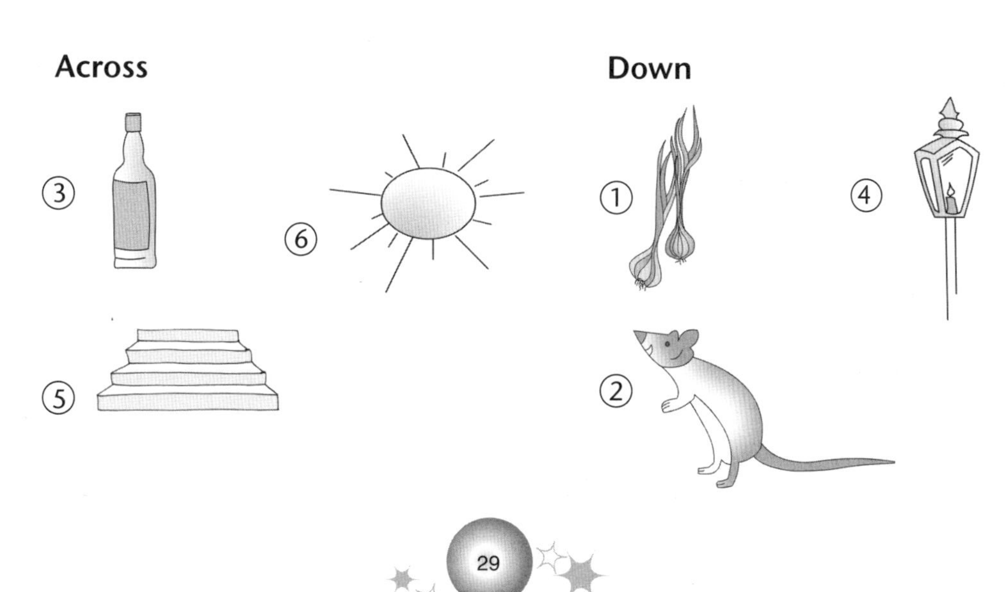

TALE OF TWO TRAINERS!

There is a pair of identical trainers in this group.
Look carefully and draw a circle around the two that are exactly the same.

FILLING STATION!

The first and last letters of some five letter words are given below. How many can you think of? To start you off, the first word could be GRAPE.

G _ _ _ **E**

G _ _ _ E

G _ _ _ E

G _ _ _ E

G _ _ _ E

G _ _ _ E

G _ _ _ E

G _ _ _ E

G _ _ _ E

G _ _ _ E

G _ _ _ E

G _ _ _ E

G _ _ _ E

☺ Good: 1 – 4

☺ V. Good: 5 – 8

☺ Excellent: 9 – 12

DOUBLE 'D' MUDDLE!

What do the words in the lists below have in common? They all have two Ds in them!
Can you find and circle them all in this word grid?
(Hint - Look up, down, across and diagonally)

R	B	R	W	E	L	L	S	Z	F	Y	I	Z	P	F
L	E	D	E	T	D	V	R	O	I	B	J	L	C	S
Q	J	L	P	D	Q	U	D	L	F	T	Y	V	P	C
R	M	R	D	H	D	D	B	S	T	S	P	A	G	D
V	B	I	F	D	E	E	G	W	G	W	P	X	W	E
T	P	D	U	R	O	E	N	S	E	M	D	Z	S	Z
L	U	D	I	K	L	T	R	Y	V	G	A	E	X	K
Q	S	L	F	D	E	L	D	D	A	T	T	Y	X	Y
P	H	E	D	Q	V	I	J	Q	G	T	G	S	W	N
H	C	U	U	Y	S	V	N	Z	E	C	M	J	I	O
U	F	W	A	D	D	L	E	V	L	B	J	W	M	A
Z	K	V	F	C	L	T	N	B	D	A	X	O	M	I
O	E	E	A	O	K	G	U	O	D	T	N	F	P	P
E	L	D	D	A	R	T	S	E	I	X	X	X	Q	P
W	F	R	A	F	S	W	N	Q	M	W	F	F	O	B

FODDER
REDDEN
WADDLE

ADDLE
MIDDLE
TODDLER

FUDDLE
STRADDLE
RIDDLE

A CLASS ACT!

Can you remember all that you see? Well, let's find out!
Study this picture carefully and then turn the page to answer some questions.
No peeking back at this page though!

QUESTIONS

1. What subject is being taught in class?
2. How many apples are on the table?
3. What date is written on the blackboard?
4. Is the teacher wearing spectacles?
5. How many girls have ponytails?
6. Are the boys' ties spotted or striped?
7. Are there any birds singing outside?
8. How many children know the answer?
9. Is someone watching from the hallway?
10. Is there a calendar on the wall?

WORD TRIANGLE!

Starting from the top, move down each step adding one letter as you go then rearrange all the letters around the 'F' to make a new word every time.

GUESS WHAT!

Here's a mystery picture for you to identify.
Just draw what you see in each of the numbered boxes below into the blank boxes which have the same number on the opposite page.

1	2	3
4	5	6
7	8	9

LETTER MAZE!

These letters make a word when they are put in the right order. Track each letter along its path and then write it in its correct place to find out what the word is.

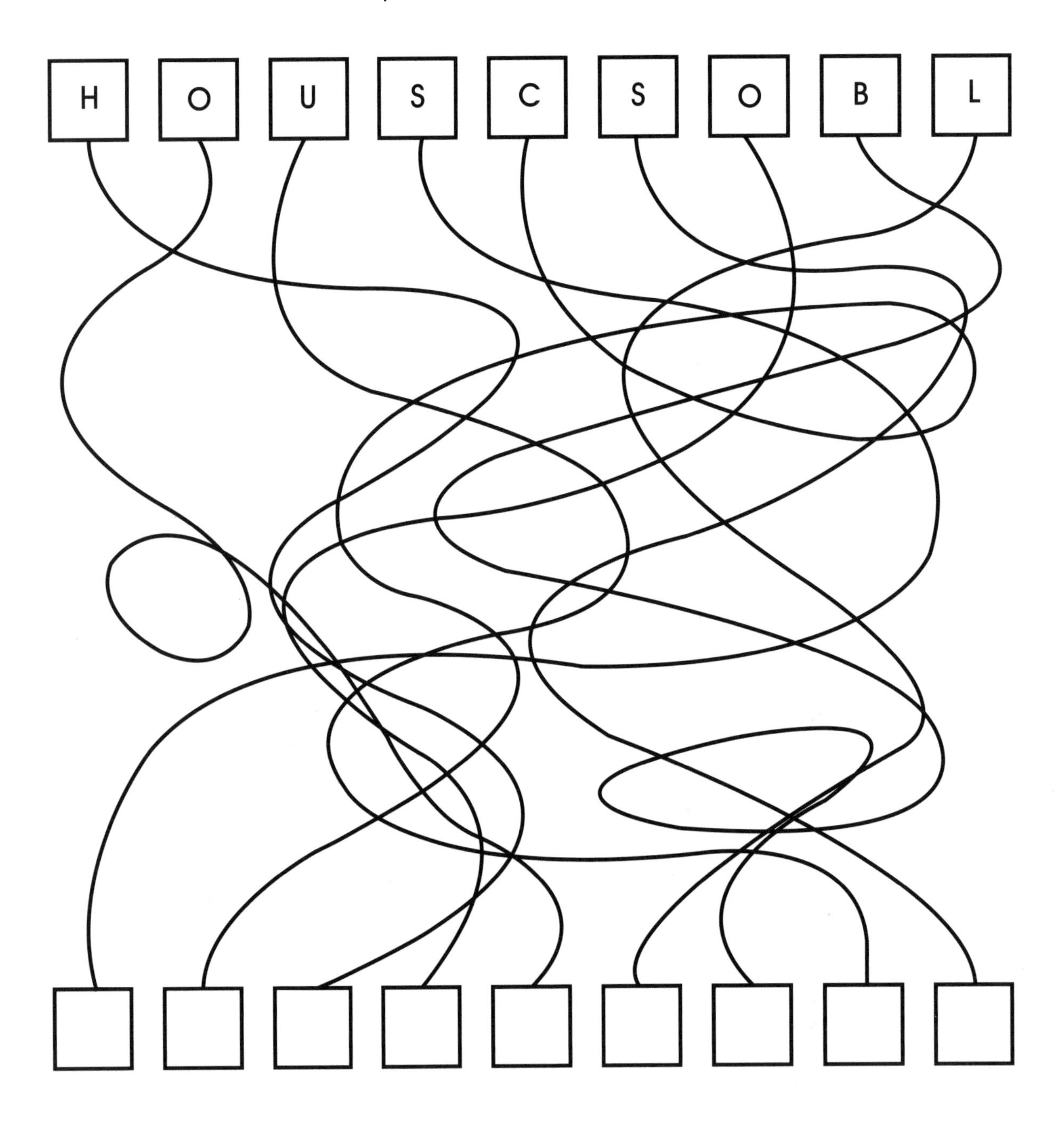

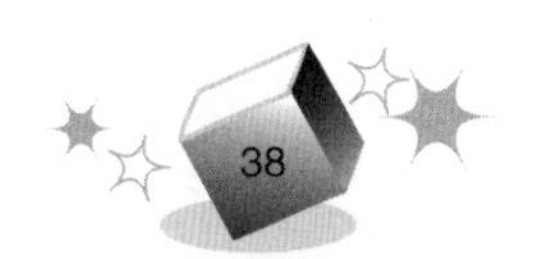

FIVE-LEGGED WONDER!

Is this elephant so heavy that it has five legs instead of four?
Or are your eyes playing tricks? Check it out!

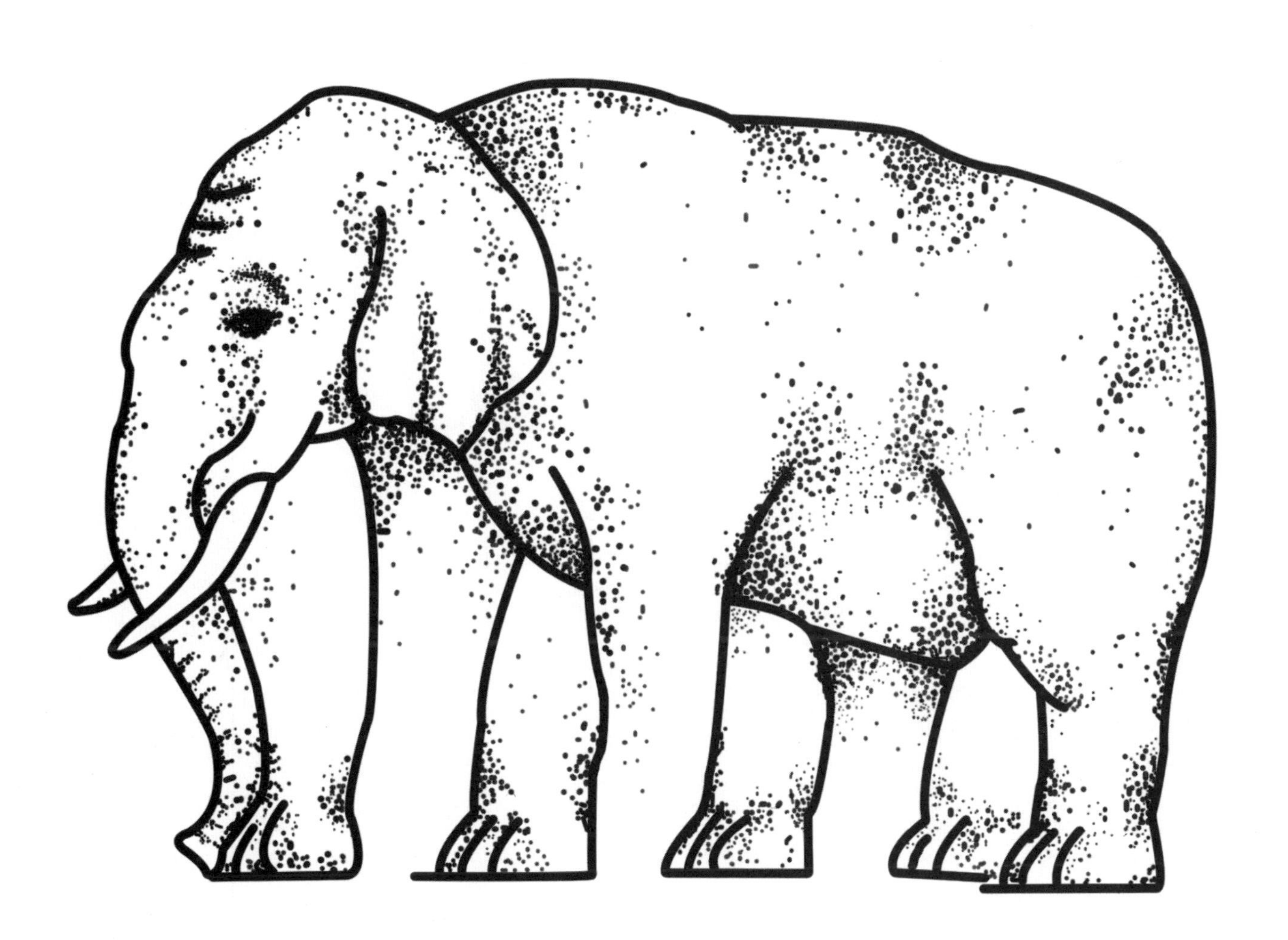

FUN AT THE PARK!

The park is a great place to spend time. And while you are there, can you find all the objects listed below that are hidden in this picture?

Balloon

Butterfly

Candyfloss

Dinosaur

Globe

Peacock feather

Piano keys

Shark fin

The digit 11

Umbrella

SEE AND SOLVE!

How good are you at reading pictures? You had better be good!
Use the visual hints to correctly fill in the words in this picture crossword.

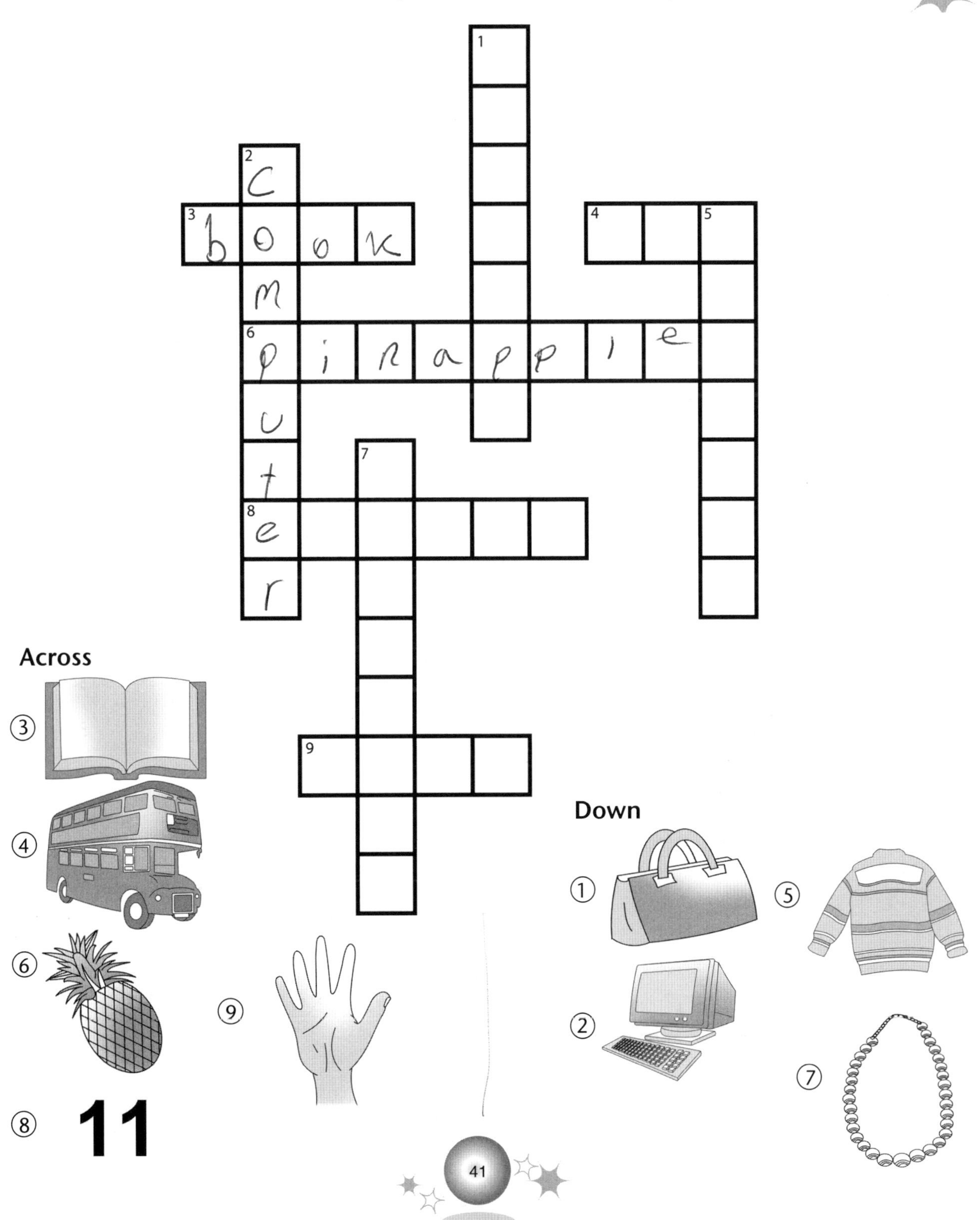

TURKEY TWINS!

There are two identical turkeys on this page.
Look carefully and draw a circle around the two that are exactly the same.

FIRST AND LAST!

The first and last letters of some five letter words are given below.
How many can you think of? To start you off, the first word could be OCCUR.

O _ _ _ R

O _ _ _ R

O _ _ _ R

O _ _ _ R

O _ _ _ R

O _ _ _ R

O _ _ _ R

O _ _ _ R

O _ _ _ R

O _ _ _ R

Good: 1 – 3

V. Good: 4 – 7

Excellent: 8 – 10

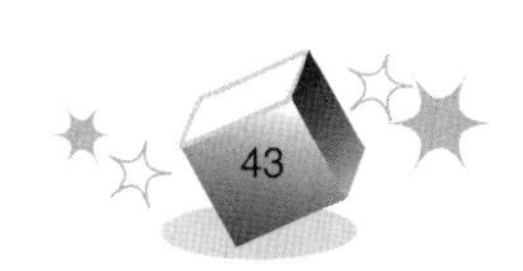

GLOBETROTTER!

Get ready for a world trip! Take a look at the list of the countries given below. Can you find and circle them in this word grid?
(*Hint - Look up, down, across and diagonally*)

M	N	F	E	B	F	Q	N	I	E	Y	K	T	J	W
T	O	O	Q	A	E	L	G	R	R	Z	N	C	T	Z
F	H	D	U	F	R	L	O	R	P	K	A	O	Y	D
R	H	J	G	G	P	P	G	A	C	N	I	M	M	N
J	C	I	B	N	A	O	F	I	I	S	L	C	A	R
I	Y	Z	E	G	I	R	N	Y	U	K	A	A	W	L
L	D	H	N	U	A	K	B	Z	D	M	R	N	G	Y
O	U	I	K	N	D	I	D	T	W	I	T	A	D	S
R	S	N	C	D	N	I	U	E	A	B	S	D	J	C
Y	S	E	C	X	S	A	C	L	T	U	U	A	Y	S
R	P	F	L	N	A	W	I	A	T	I	A	O	L	I
V	B	M	L	V	B	P	B	D	O	N	N	M	A	T
G	E	R	M	A	N	Y	K	I	N	I	V	U	T	Y
V	W	H	I	O	G	M	Y	M	P	I	R	H	I	C
Y	Z	C	G	U	V	V	U	J	Z	D	S	K	R	W

AUSTRALIA	BELGIUM	CANADA
FRANCE	GERMANY	INDIA
ITALY	SINGAPORE	TAIWAN
UNITED KINGDOM		

TAKE OFF!

Can you remember all that you see? Well, let's find out!
Study this picture carefully and then turn the page to answer some questions.
No peeking back at this page though!

QUESTIONS

1. Is the pilot showing a 'Thumbs Up' sign?
2. Do the pilots have headphones on?
3. Is there a 'No Smoking' sign?
4. Can you see the landing strip?
5. What time is it?
6. Is the co-pilot wearing a full-sleeved shirt?
7. How many people are there in the picture?
8. Is there a glass of water in the picture?
9. Are both the pilots wearing caps?
10. What is written on the steward's sleeve?

STEP LETTER!

Starting from the top, move down each step adding one letter as you go then rearrange all the letters around the 'I' to make a new word every time.

GROWING WONDER!

Here's a mystery picture for you to identify.
Just draw what you see in each of the numbered boxes below into the blank boxes which have the same number on the opposite page.

1	2	3
4	5	6
7	8	9

TRACK THE TRAIL!

These letters make a word when they are put in the right order.
Track each letter along its path and then write it in its correct place to find out what the word is.

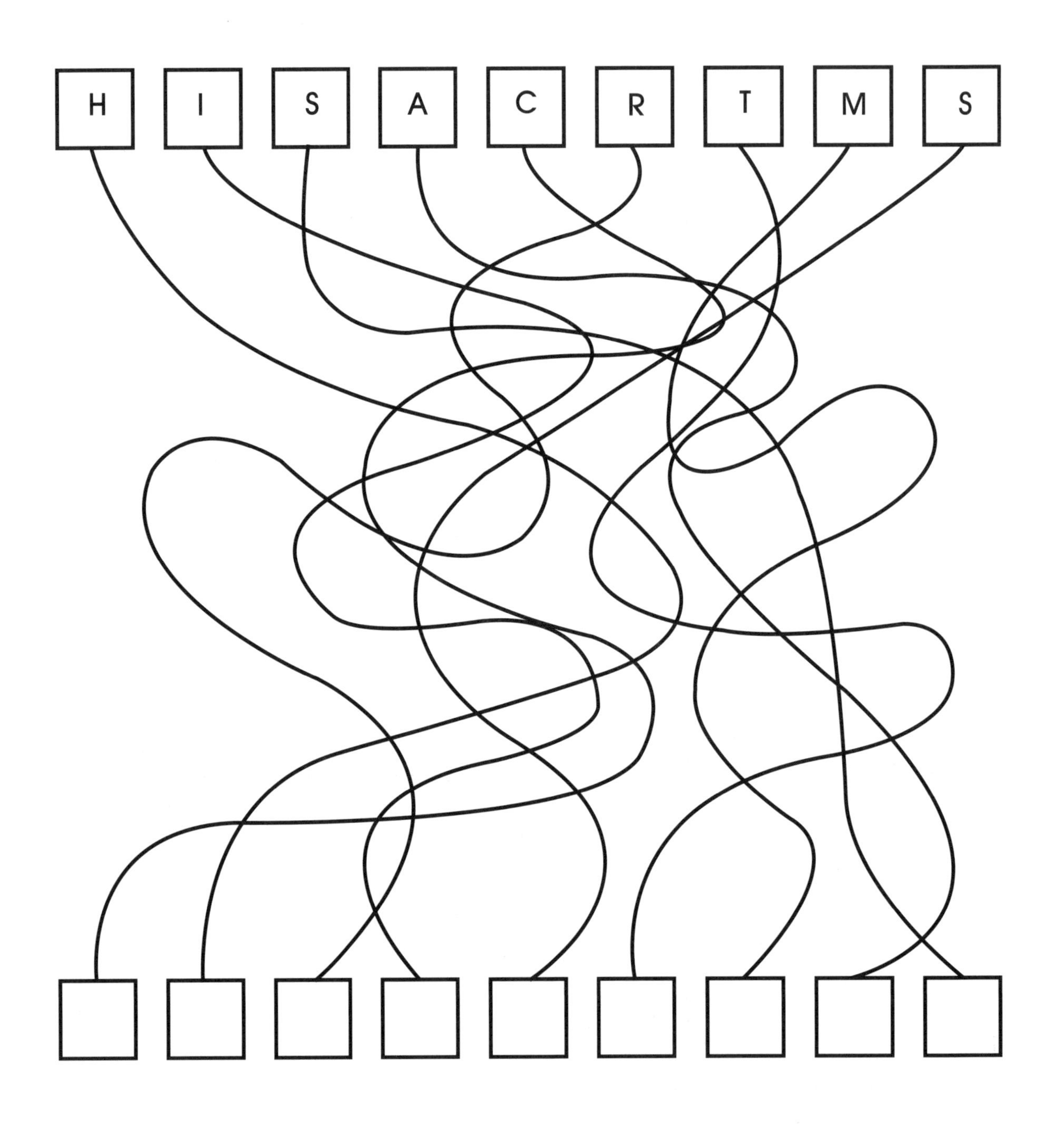

A WHEELIE!

Stare at the centre of the circle for 30 seconds...is the spiral coiling inward or growing outward?

¡ SCREAM! YOU SCREAM!

The ice-cream van is here!
Can you find all the objects that are listed below hidden in this picture?

Bird's nest

Cricket ball

Dalmatian

Dish antenna

Elephant

Frisbee

Ice-cream cone

Megaphone

Pencil

Skis

X-WORDS!

How good are you at reading pictures?
You had better be good! Use the visual hints to
correctly fill in the words in this picture crossword.

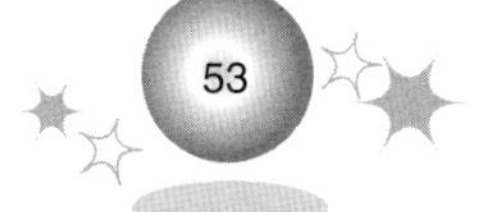

DOUBLE DECKER?!

Here is a group of double decker buses.
Look carefully and draw a circle around the two that are exactly the same.

WHAT COMES HERE?

The first and last letters of some five letter words are given below.
How many can you think of? To start you off, the first word could be PASTE.

P _ _ _ E

P _ _ _ E

P _ _ _ E

P _ _ _ E

P _ _ _ E

P _ _ _ E

P _ _ _ E

P _ _ _ E

P _ _ _ E

P _ _ _ E

P _ _ _ E

P _ _ _ E

P _ _ _ E

P _ _ _ E

P _ _ _ E

Good: 1 – 5

V. Good: 6 – 10

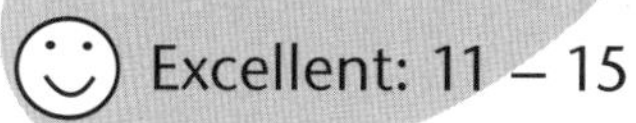

STAR PLAYERS!

Make an impressive score in this game! Look at the list of famous players from different sports. Can you find and circle them in this word grid? (*Hint-We have used first names and surnames. Look up, down, across and diagonally*)

R	N	E	X	K	R	N	L	M	V	A	A	L	G	J
L	E	A	K	V	X	O	E	P	R	P	A	N	X	S
J	P	H	D	F	B	S	C	A	E	M	O	H	H	T
B	V	P	C	R	Q	Y	L	L	R	R	M	F	K	E
T	L	Y	Q	A	O	T	F	X	T	F	E	Y	R	F
B	X	Q	B	H	M	J	P	S	Q	X	N	A	A	F
J	Y	B	S	M	E	U	M	S	A	I	T	A	K	I
V	G	F	A	D	D	R	H	H	W	R	G	Q	L	T
B	E	C	K	H	A	M	O	C	V	A	W	Y	U	N
A	N	E	R	E	S	S	K	N	S	R	Z	G	D	A
F	P	C	L	D	E	N	D	S	A	J	Y	D	N	Q
F	Q	O	G	U	W	G	I	B	A	L	N	J	E	V
N	S	A	Q	F	L	K	L	M	T	T	D	K	T	A
B	E	P	K	I	L	T	G	C	H	V	L	O	J	E
K	C	J	O	H	T	Z	F	D	A	B	W	V	E	D

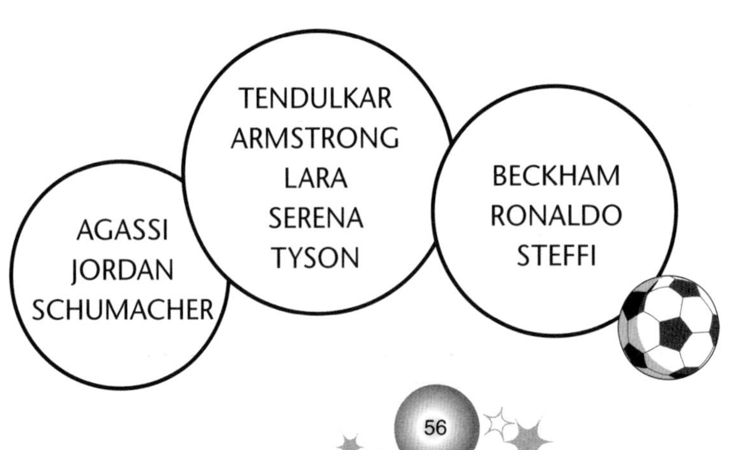

A FiELD DAY!

Can you remember all that you see? Well, let's find out!
Study this picture carefully and then turn the page to answer some questions.
No peeking back at this page though!

QUESTIONS

1. Is the farmer wearing a bandana?
2. Are the oxen standing or sitting?
3. What fruit is hanging from the trees?
4. What birds are flying in the sky?
5. What is the dog chasing?
6. What kind of a hat is the scare-crow wearing?
7. What is written on the tractor?
8. How many buckets are lying about?
9. What is the little boy doing?
10. Where is the lunch basket?

ONE AT A TIME!

Starting from the top, move down each step adding one letter as you go then rearrange all the letters around the 'O' to make a new word every time.

DRAW AND GUESS!

Here's a mystery picture for you to identify.
Just draw what you see in each of the numbered boxes below into the blank boxes which have the same number on the opposite page.

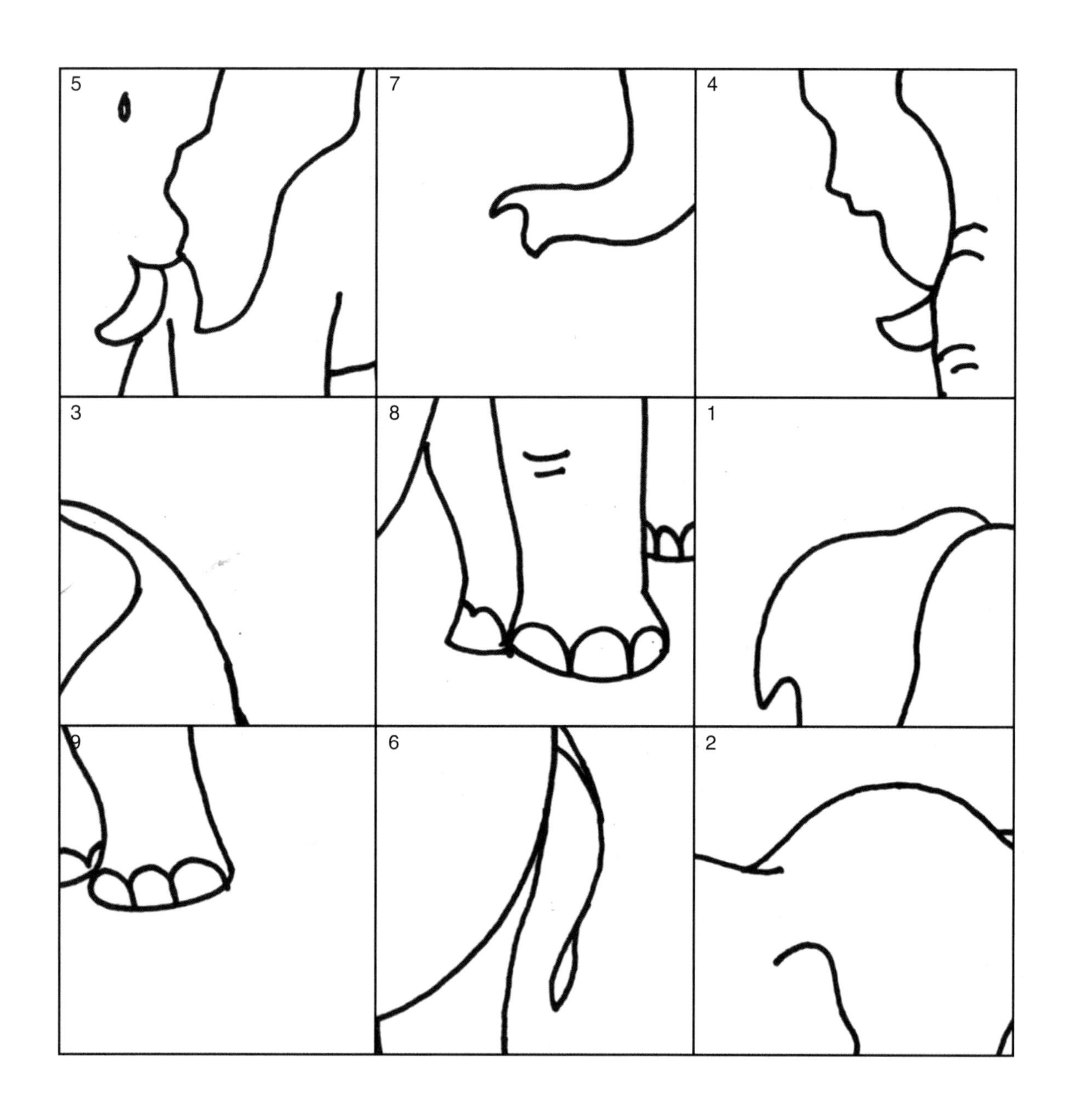

1	2	3
4	5	6
7	8	9

JUMBLE JAMBOREE!

These letters make a word when they are put in the right order.
Track each letter along its path and then write it in its
correct place to find out what the word is.

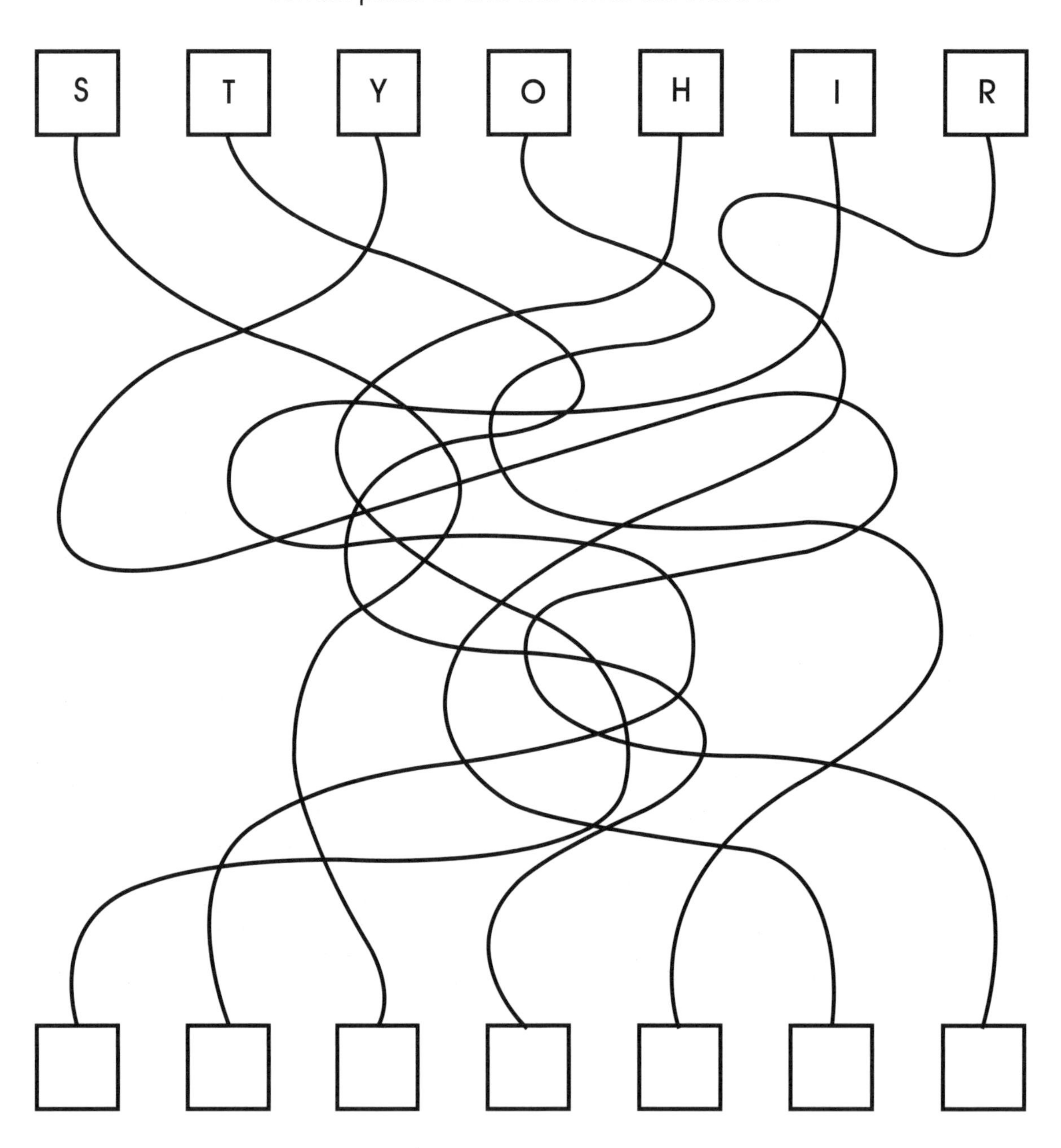

GO DOTTY!

All you have to do is stare at this grid. Can you see white dots? Or are they black? Well, it is for you to find out.

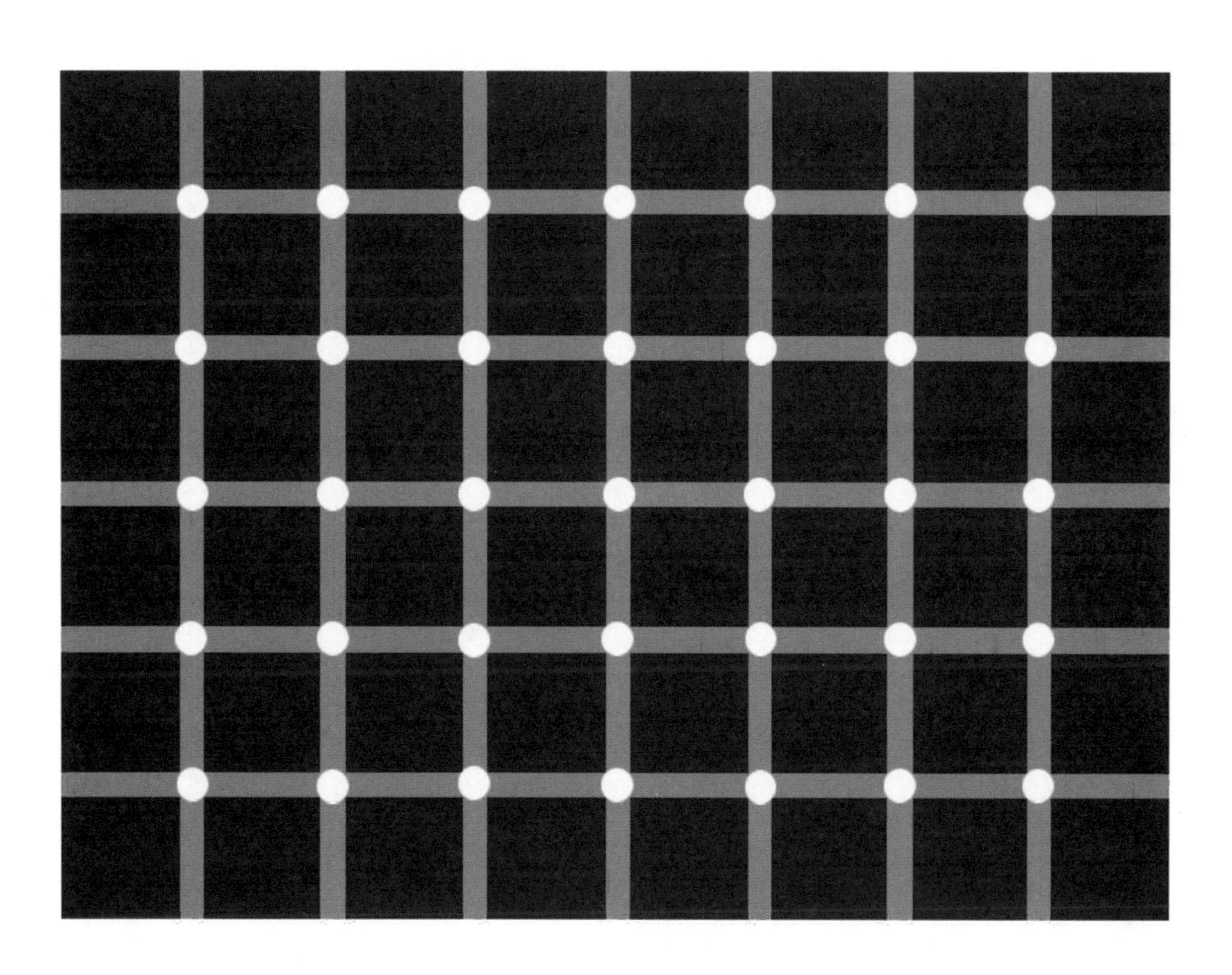

FOR SALE!

Check out this used-car showroom for a good deal.
Then look for all the objects listed below that are hidden in this picture.

- Accordion
- Basketball
- Binoculars
- Chess board
- Computer mouse
- Pizza slice
- Suitcase
- Sign for 10,000
- Thermos flask
- The letter H

ACROSS AND DOWN!

How good are you at reading pictures?
You had better be good!
Use the visual hints to correctly fill in the words in this picture crossword.

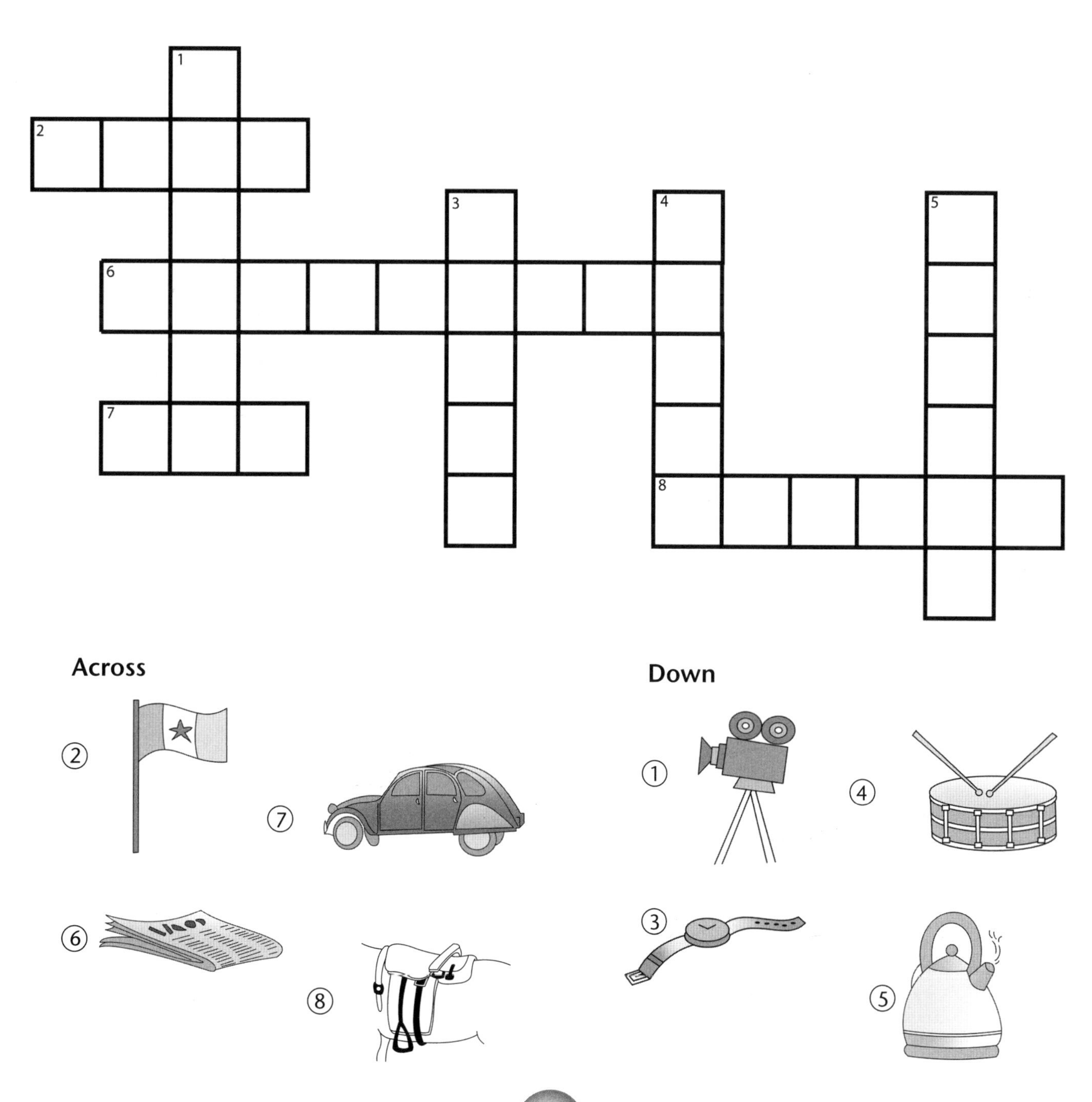

ROSE REPLICAS!

Can you find two identical roses in this group?
Look carefully and draw a circle around the two that are exactly the same.

WORD VARIATION!

The first and last letters of some five letter words are given below. How many can you think of? To start you off, the first word could be ACTOR.

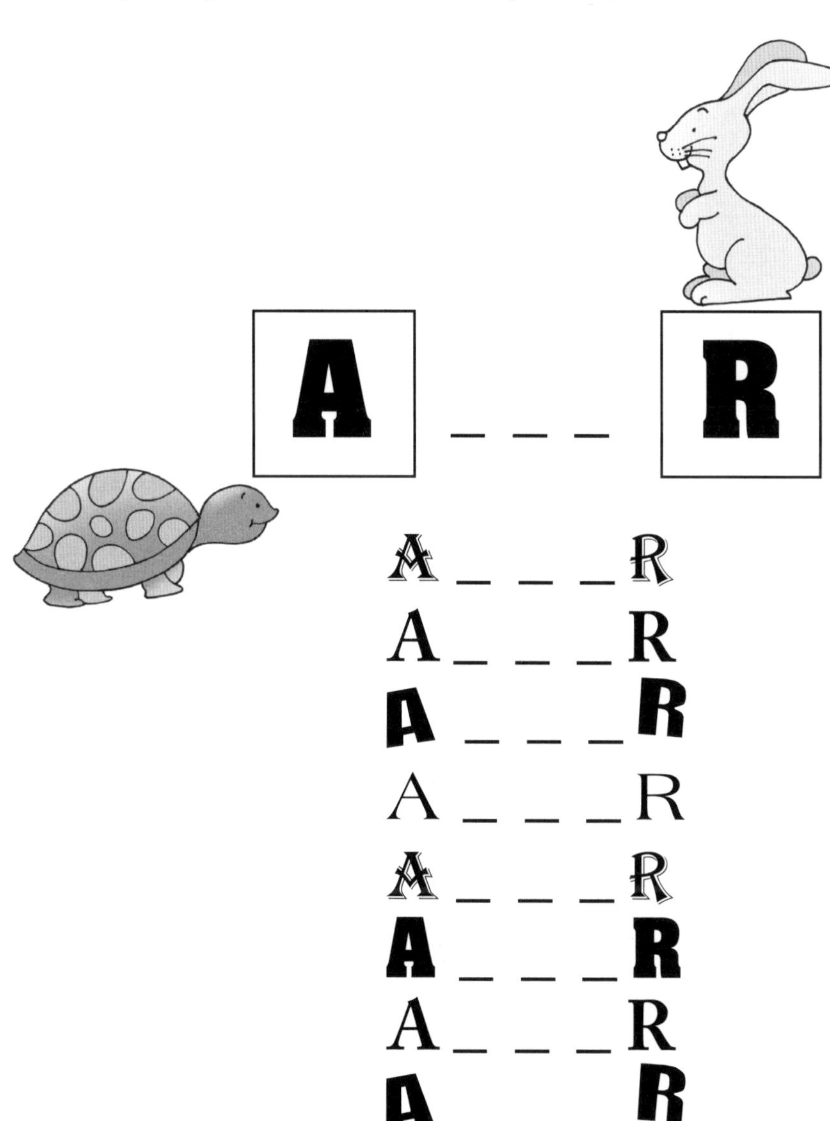

A _ _ _ R

A _ _ _ R

A _ _ _ R

A _ _ _ R

A _ _ _ R

A _ _ _ R

A _ _ _ R

A _ _ _ R

A _ _ _ R

Good: 1 – 3

V. Good: 4 – 7

Excellent: 8 – 10

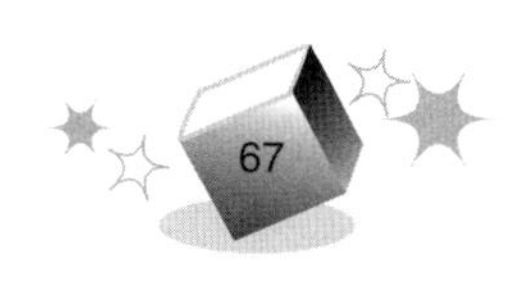

TREE TRAP!

There are so many types of trees in here.
Read the list below, then find and circle all the tree names in this word grid.
(*Hint - Look up, down, across and diagonally*)

P	X	D	Y	Y	U	W	K	Y	B	A	M	G	F	T
Q	O	U	K	W	Q	I	A	A	I	S	B	I	L	U
W	X	P	Q	H	F	L	K	W	O	E	T	R	U	N
O	F	T	L	G	Q	L	B	H	E	P	T	G	E	T
Y	B	O	X	A	G	O	Y	C	U	S	I	G	H	S
N	X	B	R	T	R	W	H	C	V	H	D	S	J	E
G	S	D	Y	C	W	A	L	N	U	T	A	X	T	H
P	L	U	J	H	I	K	A	E	T	V	Q	Q	D	C
X	Y	F	X	L	C	Q	F	W	X	S	F	W	E	L
N	L	W	G	S	J	B	B	L	S	A	X	M	Q	G
E	E	D	Z	G	E	U	K	E	E	J	R	V	B	K
O	K	U	U	T	V	V	R	F	D	B	K	B	M	H
T	W	G	F	Q	J	P	K	Y	F	U	C	N	L	S
S	K	M	G	W	Y	E	J	L	K	N	T	J	E	T
E	Z	F	Z	C	S	Z	M	J	D	K	T	L	O	E

ASH	BEECH	CHESTNUT
CYPRESS	ELM	OAK
POPLAR	TEAK	WALNUT
WILLOW		

WHAT'S COOKING?

Can you remember all that you see? Well, let's find out!
Study this picture carefully and then turn the page to answer some questions.
No peeking back at this page though!

QUESTIONS

1. Is the frying pan on the stove?
2. What is written on the apron?
3. Is the microwave oven beeping?
4. How many fridge magnets are stuck on the fridge?
5. Are the pieces of toast done?
6. What is mother chopping?
7. Is there a baby in the high chair?
8. How many eggs are there in the egg tray?
9. Is a cabinet door open?
10. Are there teacups on the tray?

WORD PYRAMID!

Starting from the top, move down each step adding one letter as you go then rearrange all the letters around the 'T' to make a new word every time.

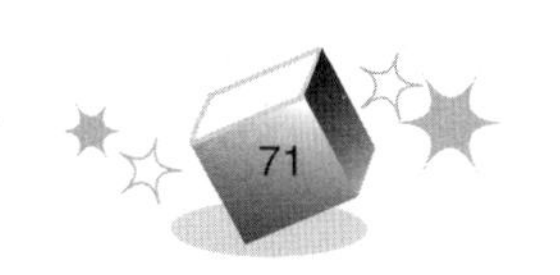

PICTURE IN PARTS!

Here's a mystery picture for you to identify.
Just draw what you see in each of the numbered boxes below into the blank boxes which have the same number on the opposite page.

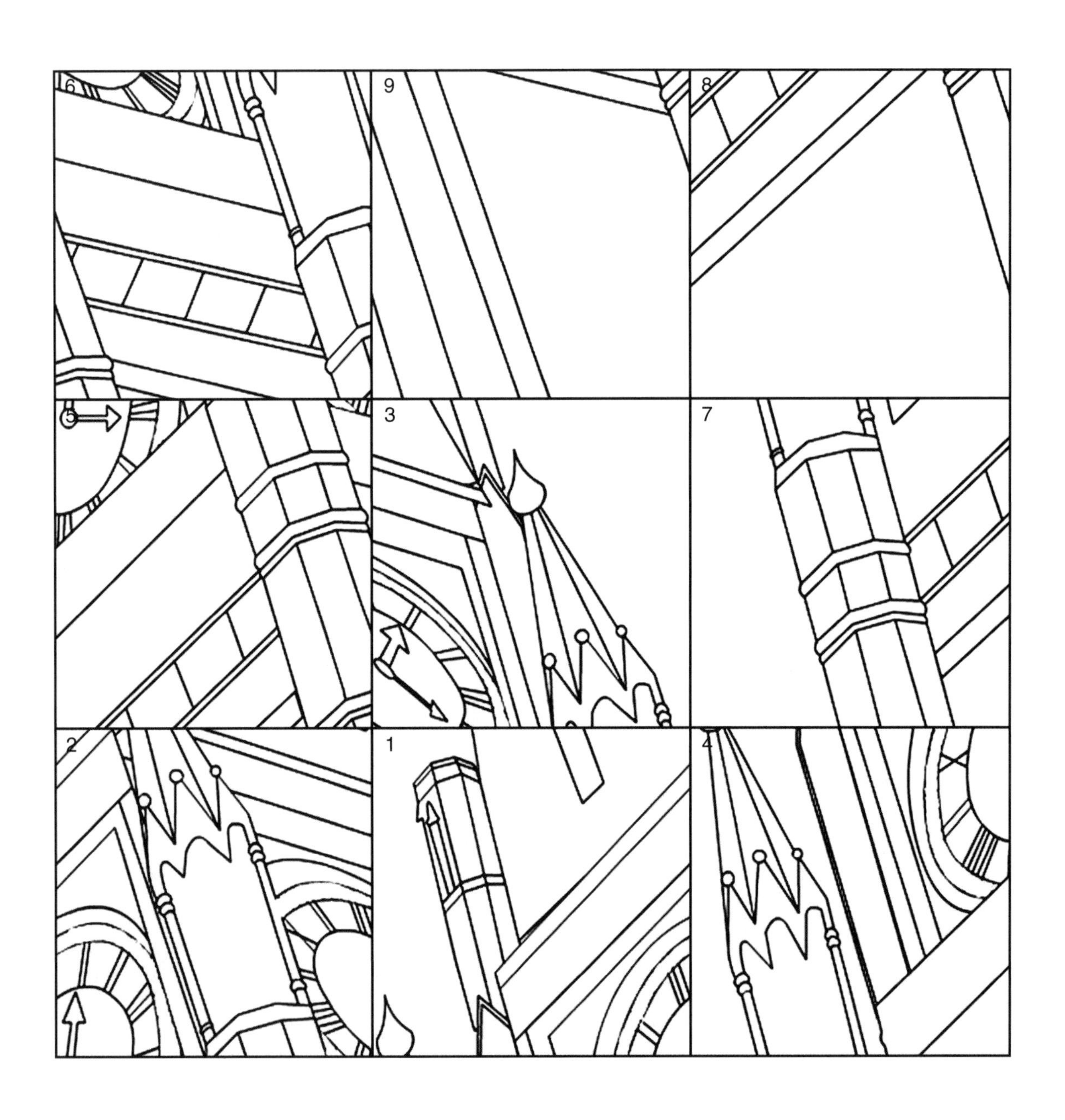

1	2	3
4	5	6
7	8	9

LETTER ROUTE!

These letters make a word when they are put in the right order. Track each letter along its path and then write it in its correct place to find out what the word is.

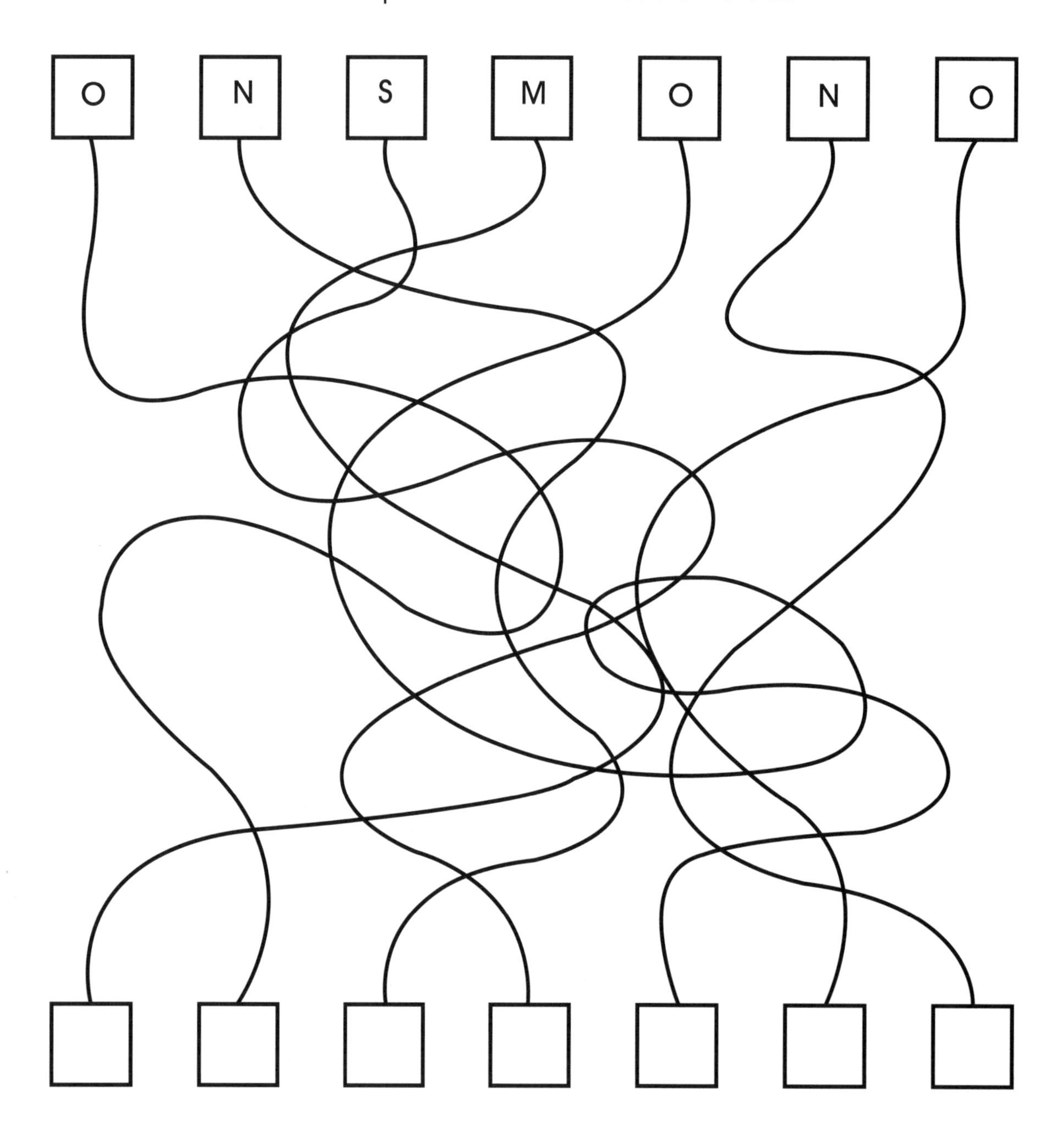

INDIAN ENIGMA!

Is this the profile of an American Indian or is this an Eskimo with his back turned? What do you think?

HERE WE GO!

All packed for your holiday? Just to double check, look at the list below then find all the objects hidden in this picture.

- Arrow
- Feeding bottle
- Heart
- Orange
- Ribbon
- Shark
- Skipping rope
- Slate
- Spectacles
- Paper clip

CLUE CONNECTION!

How good are you at reading pictures?
You had better be good! Use the visual hints to correctly
fill in the words in this picture crossword.

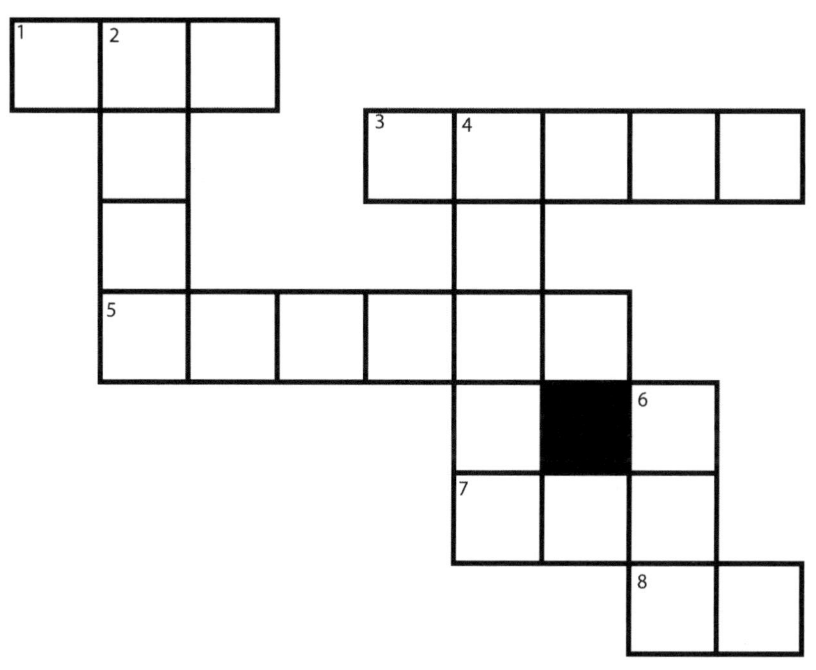

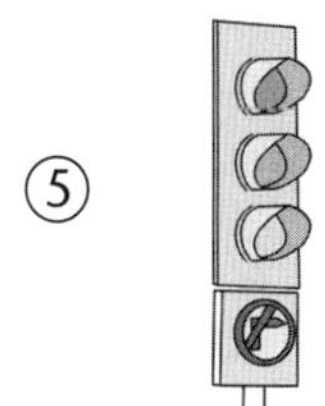

PIZZA PAIR!

Someone has ordered two pizzas with the same toppings.
Look carefully and draw a circle around the two that are exactly the same.

MESS IN THE MIDDLE!

The first and last letters of some five letter words are given below.
How many can you think of?
To start you off, the first word could be VALUE.

_ _ _

V _ _ _ E

V _ _ _ E

V _ _ _ E

V _ _ _ E

V _ _ _ E

☺	Good:	1 – 3
☺	V. Good:	4 – 5
☺	Excellent:	6 – 7

FISHING FUN!

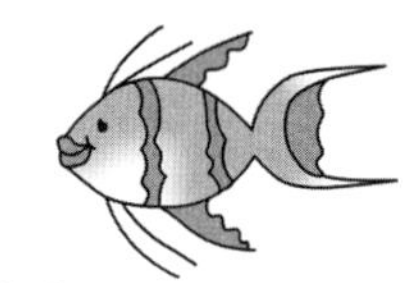

Are they biting yet? Read the list below and get set to fish in this word grid. Look up, down, across and diagonally to find and circle all of them.

H	A	A	C	K	E	W	E	U	D	Y	I	I	T	O
L	S	J	T	M	Z	H	D	Q	L	N	J	P	U	Y
B	W	I	Z	N	W	A	Y	Y	O	Q	J	I	C	I
W	K	N	F	T	L	L	J	A	M	W	Y	R	J	W
G	A	V	F	D	R	E	D	P	R	P	A	N	U	T
V	U	N	L	J	L	O	X	F	R	E	I	Q	P	H
V	C	O	S	B	F	O	U	Z	C	V	D	N	X	Q
Q	W	M	W	K	D	E	G	T	W	H	O	Q	G	L
U	K	I	G	N	D	N	T	L	X	M	G	V	J	D
D	U	N	B	M	P	I	B	F	L	S	H	A	R	K
L	D	A	N	W	O	D	W	A	K	E	V	M	E	D
K	S	P	R	M	F	R	S	C	R	F	E	C	M	Q
S	L	U	A	K	D	A	V	X	A	Y	V	Y	G	K
A	V	I	D	K	F	S	U	J	A	Q	C	Y	G	H
C	E	X	N	D	I	Z	U	X	E	B	B	D	U	S

BASS
SALMON
TROUT

RAY
SHARK
WHALE

GOLDFISH
SARDINE
TUNA

PET SET!

Can you remember all that you see? Well, let's find out!
Study this picture carefully and then turn the page to answer some questions.
No peeking back at this page though!

QUESTIONS

1. What bird is in the cage?
2. Where is the cat?
3. What is written on the dog dish?
4. How many goldfish are there in the bowl?
5. Is there a picture frame hanging?
6. What is the turtle doing?
7. What animal is hanging from the curtains?
8. Is there a hamster in the shoe box?
9. Are there any butterflies?
10. Is the dog wearing a collar?

LUCKY SEVEN!

Starting from the top, move down each step adding one letter as you go then rearrange all the letters around the 'F' to make a new word every time.

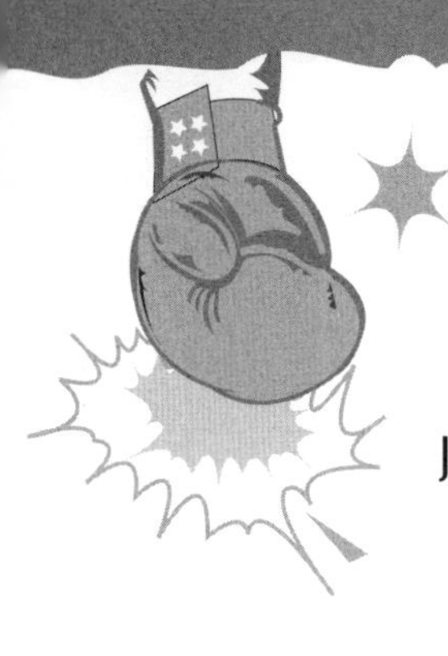

SNAP SHUFFLE!

Here's a mystery picture for you to identify.
Just draw what you see in each of the numbered boxes below into the blank boxes which have the same number on the opposite page.

1	2	3
4	5	6
7	8	9

MAZE MINGLE!

These letters make a word when they are put in the right order. Track each letter along its path and then write it in its correct place to find out what the word is.

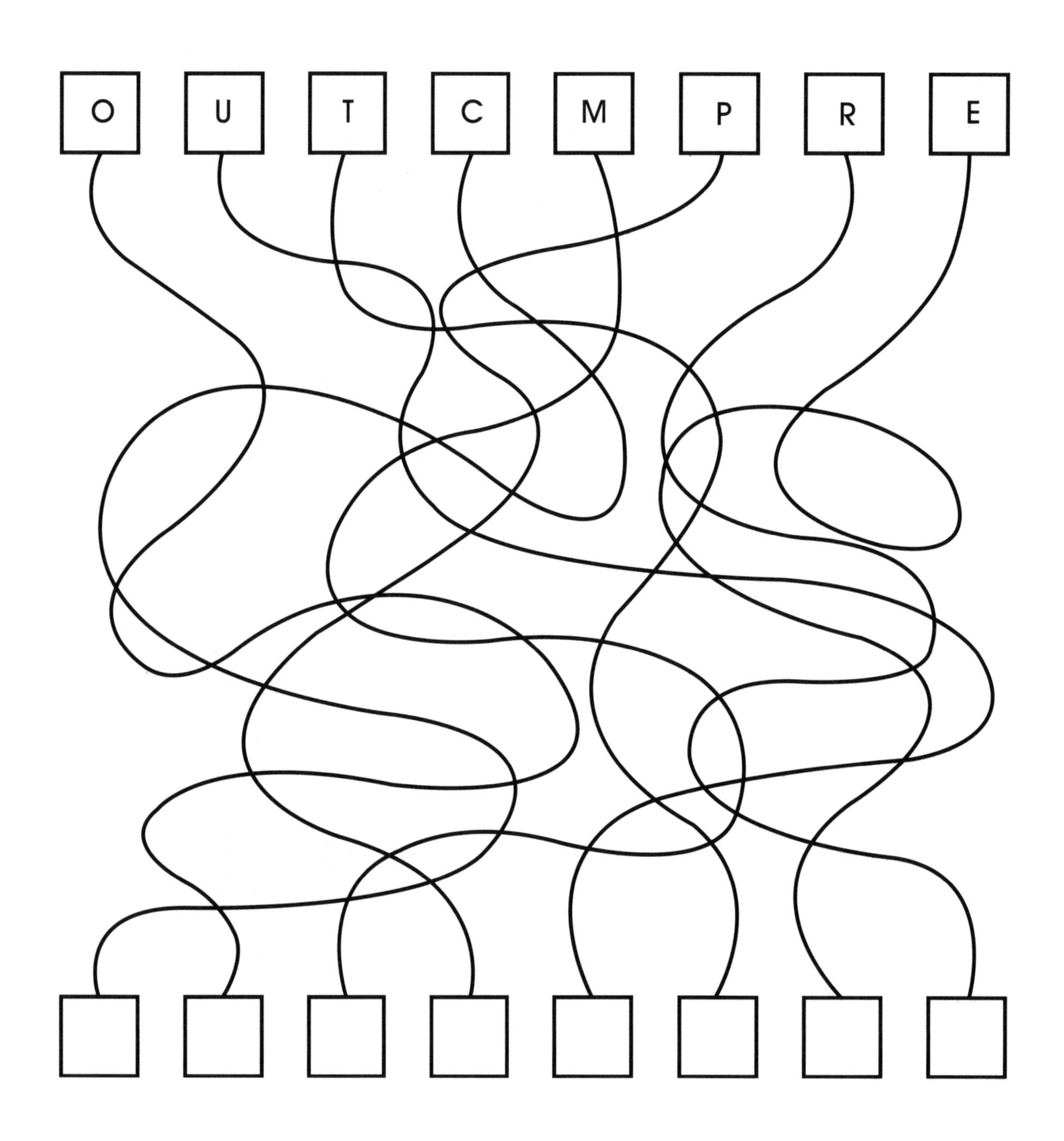

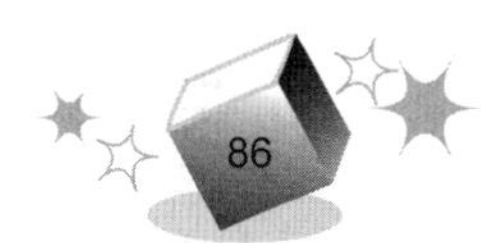

LET'S FACE IT!

Here is an image of a vase. Or are these profiles of two people facing each other? Can you tell?

SPLASH! SPLASH!

Just dive in, the water's fine!
Look for all the objects listed below that are hidden in this poolside picture.

Crocodile
Doughnut
Flag
Grape vine
Newspaper
Porthole
Snake
Suntan lotion
Sombrero
Torch

READ THE PIX!

How good are you at reading pictures?
You had better be good!
Use the visual hints to correctly fill in the words in this picture crossword.

Across

②

⑤

④

⑥

Down

①

③

④

SIMILAR SKATEBOARDS?

There are two identical skateboards in this group.
Look carefully and draw a circle around the two that are exactly the same.

FIVE LETTER FUN!

The first and last letters of some five letter words are given below. How many can you think of? To start you off, the first word could be BOOST.

B _ _ _ **T**

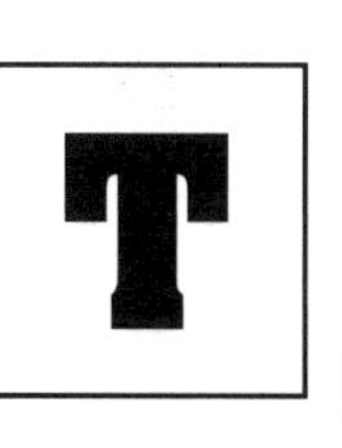

B _ _ _ T

B _ _ _ T

B _ _ _ T

B _ _ _ T

B _ _ _ T

B _ _ _ T

B _ _ _ T

B _ _ _ T

B _ _ _ T

B _ _ _ T

B _ _ _ T

☺ Good:	1 – 4
☺ V. Good:	5 – 8
☺ Excellent:	9 – 12

NOW SHOWING!

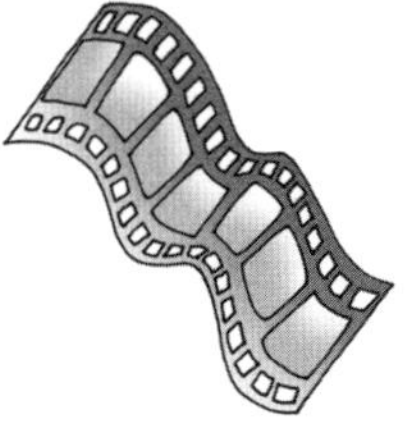

All set for the movies? Look at the list of famous blockbusters. Can you find and circle them all in this word grid? (*Hint - Look up, down, across and diagonally*)

E	Y	K	S	G	W	K	J	K	H	I	R	J	H	S
D	L	S	E	V	N	B	N	O	D	O	E	P	Y	P
D	Q	T	T	R	A	A	M	Q	M	B	T	N	N	I
L	R	I	T	C	H	E	F	E	B	W	T	X	M	D
U	H	D	D	I	A	S	N	P	O	V	O	G	I	E
T	E	M	O	L	L	G	Z	V	C	U	P	G	W	R
P	L	G	O	L	N	T	I	E	F	S	Y	U	N	M
G	H	N	C	I	I	P	R	F	D	S	R	Q	Q	A
Q	E	E	D	S	P	T	Q	A	S	J	R	O	S	N
P	U	N	R	S	Z	R	T	X	U	O	A	W	Y	Y
N	I	L	H	V	F	K	G	L	I	T	H	N	E	J
F	S	H	A	R	K	T	A	L	E	S	S	G	E	E
G	N	I	K	N	O	I	L	P	A	Z	Z	A	O	A
Z	W	P	I	X	R	W	T	D	S	W	X	Q	R	R
N	W	T	D	E	D	T	G	X	Y	L	U	L	A	N

DR. DOLITTLE
HOME ALONE
SHREK

FINDING NEMO
LION KING
SPIDERMAN

HARRY POTTER
SHARK TALES
STUART LITTLE

iT'S ONLY FAiR!

Can you remember all that you see? Well, let's find out! Study this picture carefully and then turn the page to answer some questions. No peeking back at this page though!

QUESTIONS

1. Who is buying candy floss?
2. What kind of a cycle is there in the picture?
3. Is the Ferris wheel moving?
4. How many balloons are flying off?
5. Is there a magic show at the circus?
6. Who is enjoying himself on the merry-go-round?
7. What does the banner say?
8. What does the little boy want to do?
9. Is there a stilt-walker around?
10. How much does an entry ticket cost?

WORD BUILDING!

Starting from the top, move down each step adding one letter as you go then rearrange all the letters around the 'U' to make a new word every time.

THE COUNTDOWN!

Here's a mystery picture for you to identify. Just draw what you see in each of the numbered boxes into the blank boxes which have the same number on the opposite page.

1	2	3
4	5	6
7	8	9

SCARY SCRAMBLE!

These letters make a word when they are put in the right order. Track each letter along its path and then write it in its correct place to find out what the word is.

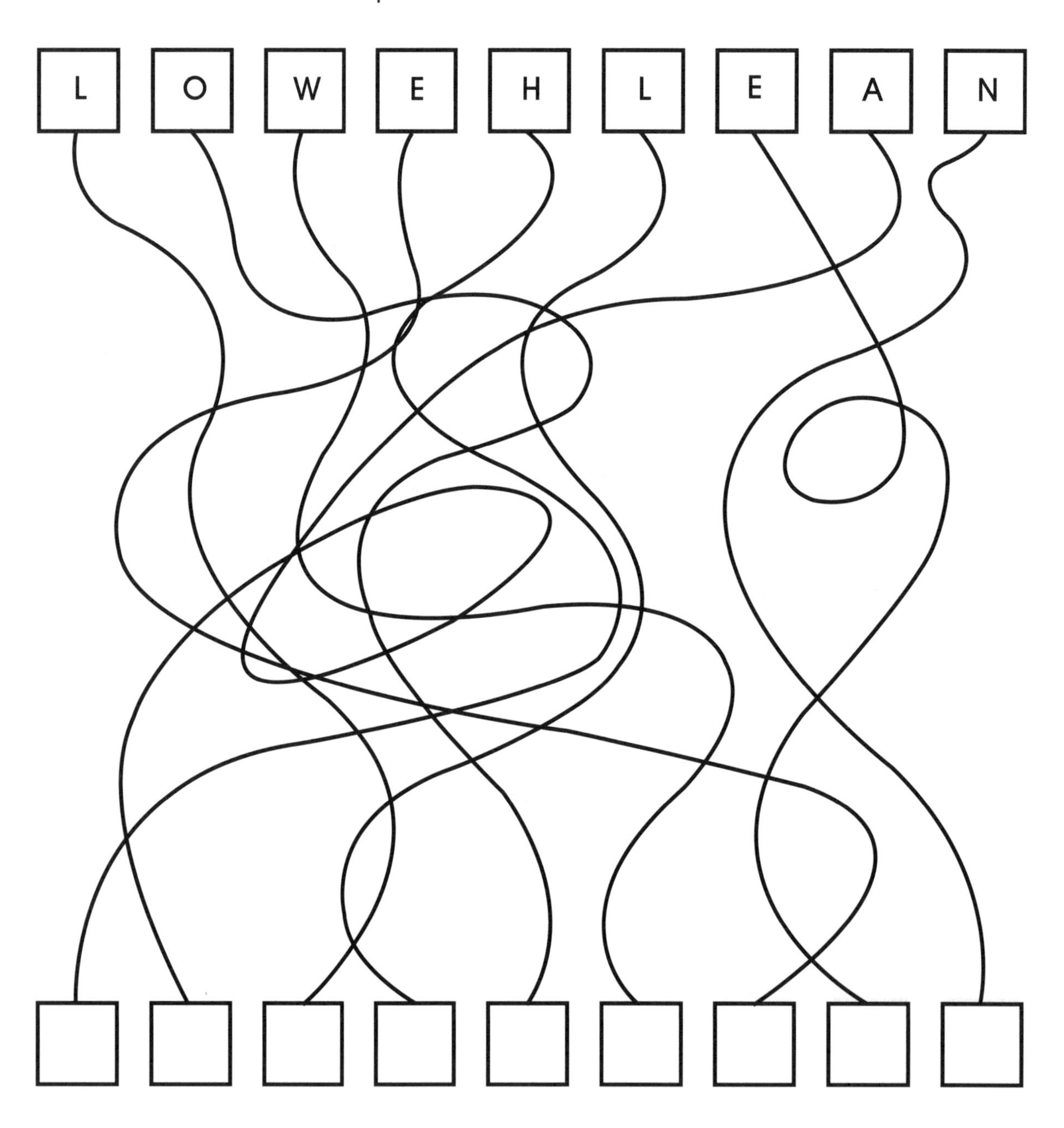

BALL ON THE ROLL!

If you stare long enough at the ball in the centre, you will find that it starts to move! Amazing isn't it?

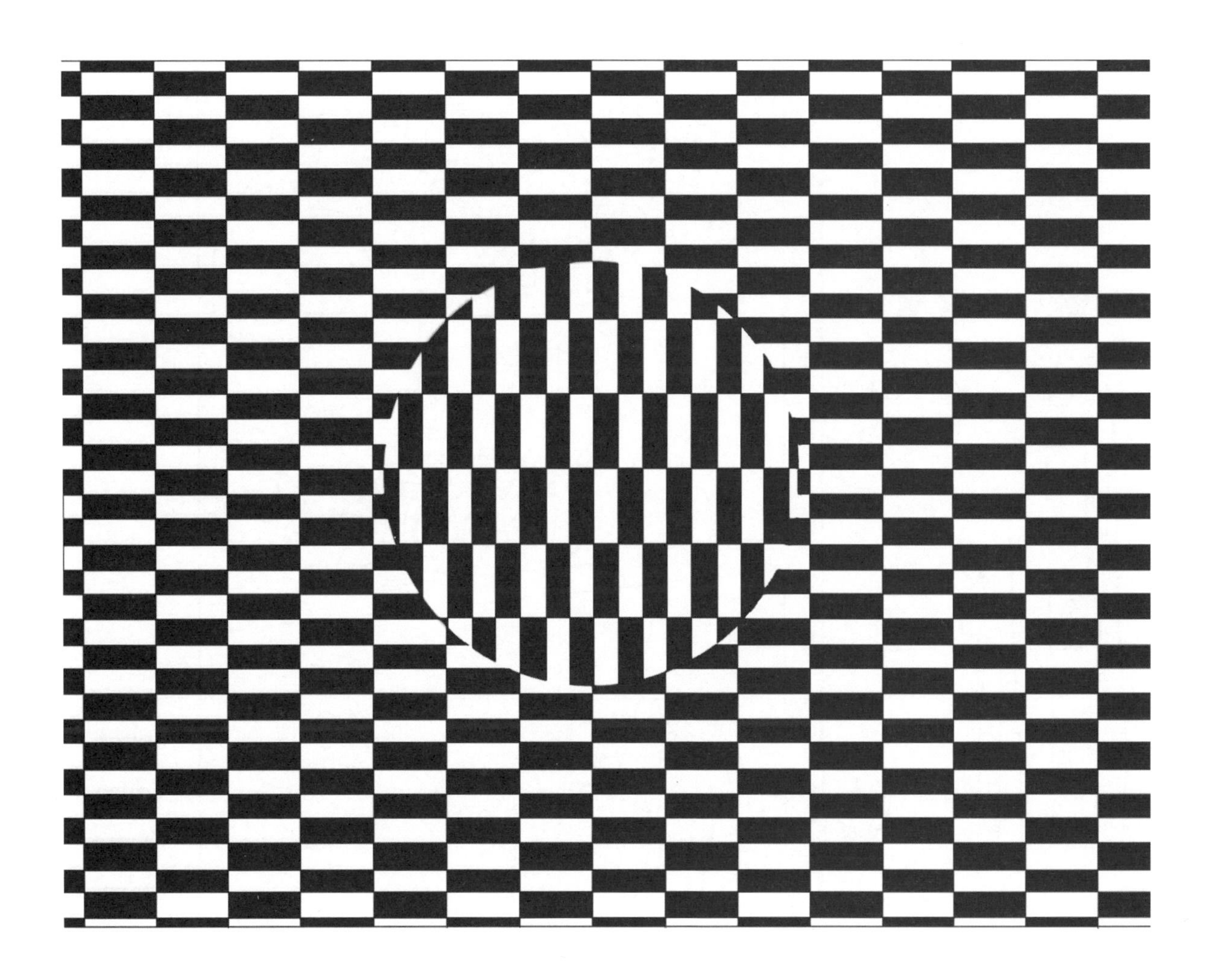

IT'S PLAYTIME!

Wow, what a toy cupboard! Can you find all the toys from the list below that are hidden in this picture?

- Button
- Coffee mug
- Curtains
- Ice-cream cone
- Rolling pin
- Santa hat
- Star
- Strawberries
- Tennis ball
- The letter S

PICTURE PLAY!

How good are you at reading pictures?
You had better be good! Use the visual hints to correctly fill in the words in this picture crossword.

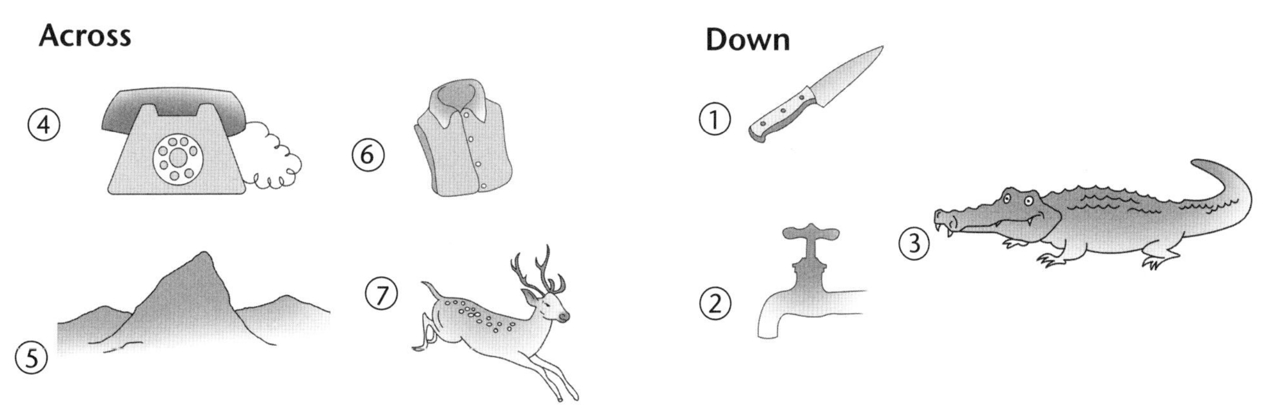

MATCHING MASKS!

There are two identical masks in this group.
Look carefully and draw a circle around the two that are exactly the same.

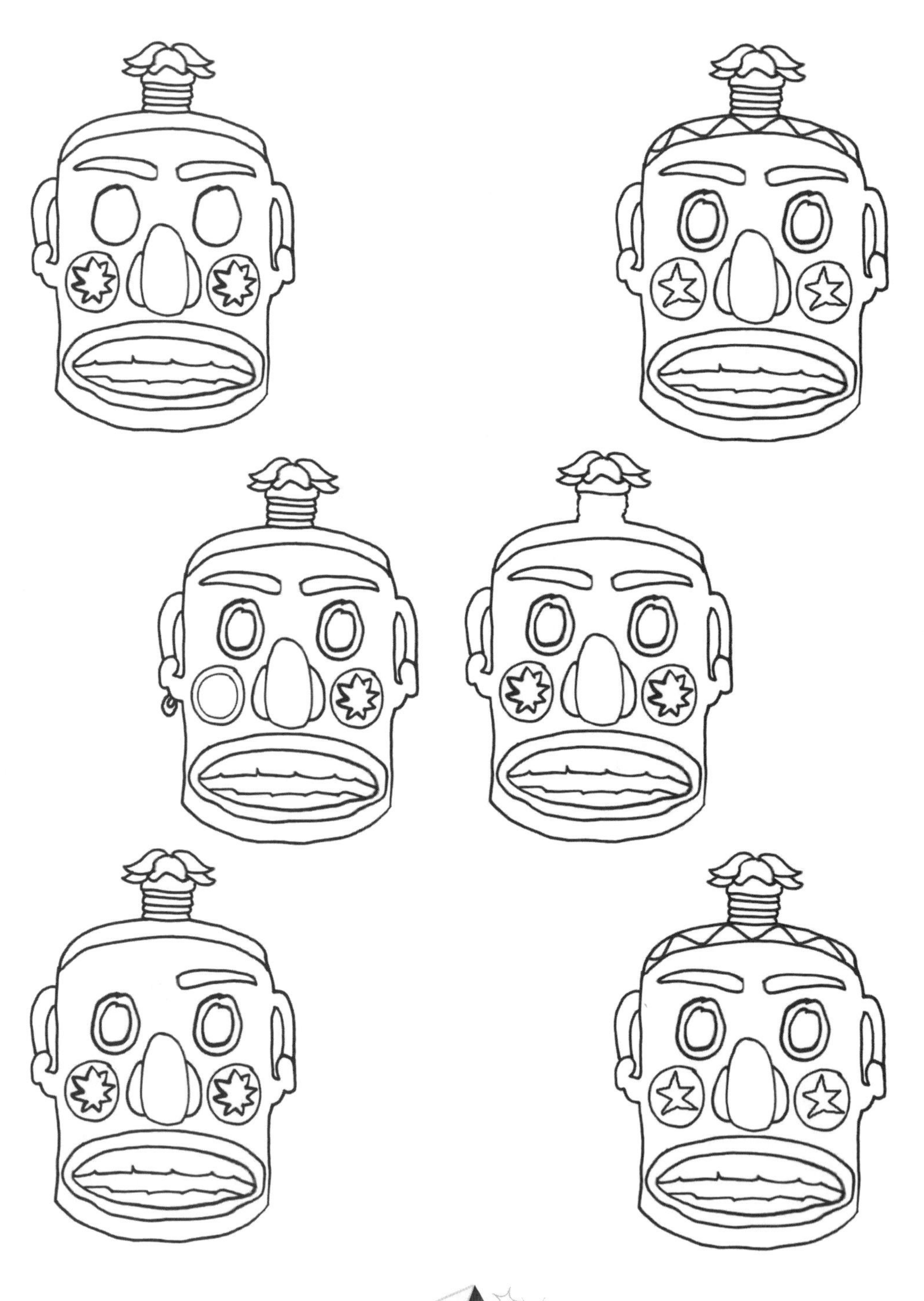

TEST YOUR WORD POWER!

The first and last letters of some five letter words are given below.
How many can you think of? To start you off, the first word could be CYCLE.

C _ _ _ E

C _ _ _ E
C _ _ _ E
C _ _ _ E
C _ _ _ E
C _ _ _ E
C _ _ _ E
C _ _ _ E
C _ _ _ E
C _ _ _ E
C _ _ _ E
C _ _ _ E
C _ _ _ E
C _ _ _ E
C _ _ _ E

Good: 1 – 5
V. Good: 6 – 10
Excellent: 11 – 15

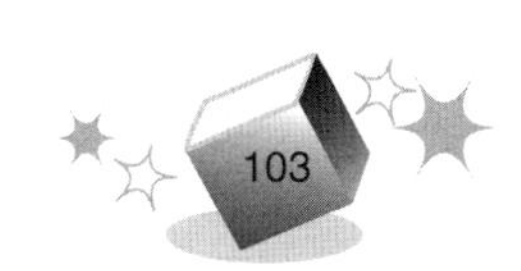

CHRISTMAS FUSS!

Take a look at the list of gifts Santa will bring if you have been good!
Can you find and circle them all in this word grid?
(*Hint - Look up, down, across and diagonally*)

B	Q	E	H	R	J	Y	U	H	Q	E	C	M	H	N
D	S	M	L	X	W	N	J	L	H	O	R	A	R	G
W	G	R	J	C	N	A	O	E	M	W	I	N	E	Q
X	C	P	C	H	Y	L	T	P	K	J	K	C	T	N
V	R	N	H	A	L	C	U	C	P	P	I	C	A	J
L	N	L	O	U	E	T	I	Q	H	M	P	C	E	Z
L	A	G	C	S	E	V	I	B	C	W	R	F	W	K
J	G	S	O	R	S	R	E	N	I	A	R	T	S	N
L	U	W	L	V	J	Q	O	J	H	O	I	E	X	G
E	X	A	A	B	O	O	K	S	V	C	H	L	P	N
T	N	Q	T	W	T	A	B	H	T	T	N	J	Y	X
F	G	B	E	T	M	C	L	X	O	G	J	M	Q	V
O	A	Q	S	D	A	X	U	L	Y	O	J	N	C	G
U	A	R	W	F	E	F	C	H	S	T	D	S	U	O
A	G	E	X	U	B	P	E	O	E	F	S	A	V	J

BICYCLE	BOOKS	CHOCOLATES
CLOTHES	COMPUTER	SWEATER
TOYS	TRAINERS	WATCH

ALL HANDS ON DECK!

Can you remember all that you see?
Well, let's find out! Study this picture carefully and then turn the page to answer some questions. No peeking back at this page though!

QUESTIONS

1. Is there a flag anywhere?
2. What is written on the airship?
3. What hat does the old woman have on?
4. Does the captain have a beard?
5. Are there any packed suitcases?
6. Is the sun overhead or on the horizon?
7. What bird is perched on the deck?
8. What is the young man ready for?
9. Who is on the crow's nest?
10. How many little children are playing?

SEVEN WORD WONDER!

Starting from the top, move down each step adding one letter as you go then rearrange all the letters around the 'M' to make a new word every time.

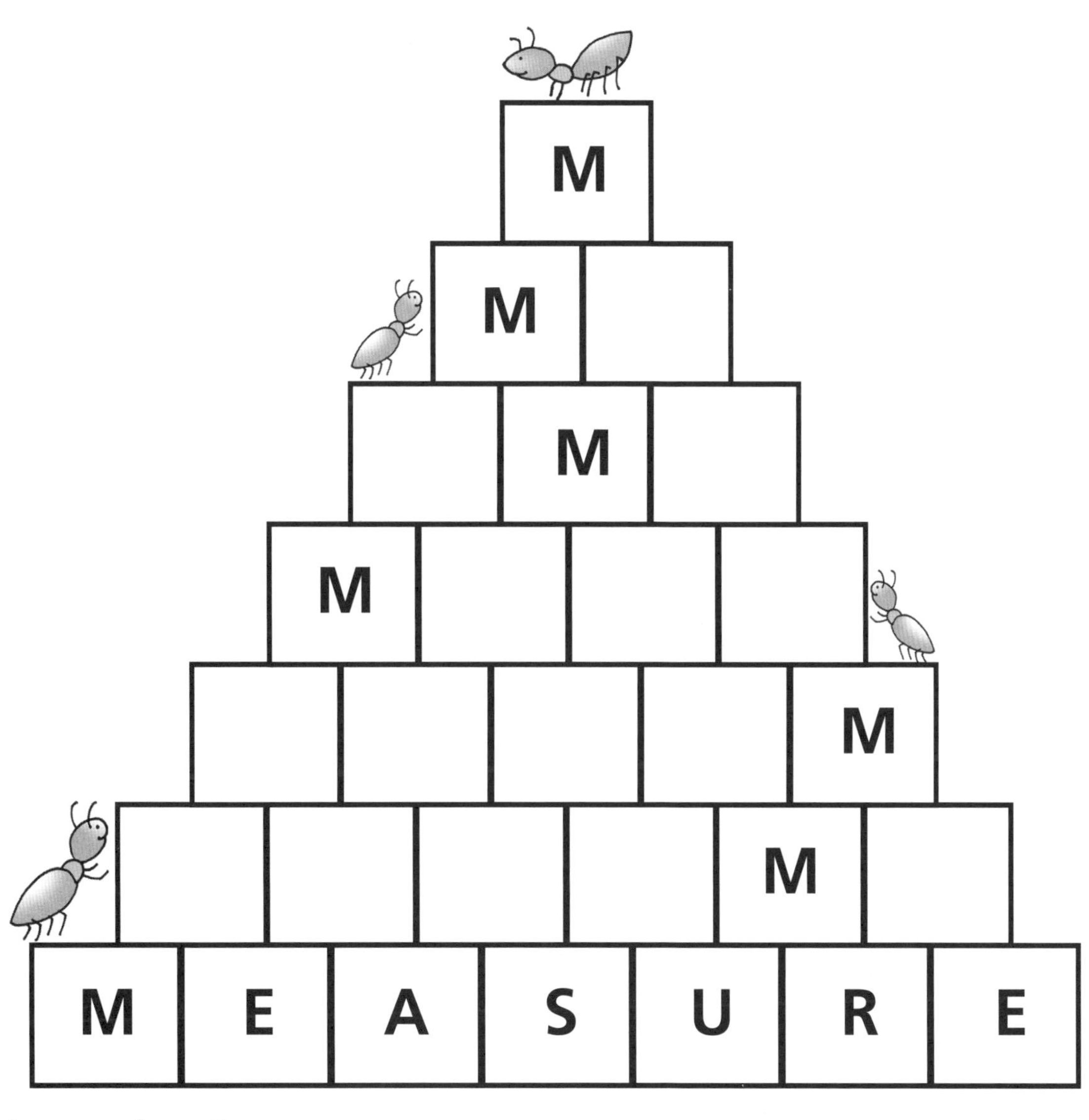

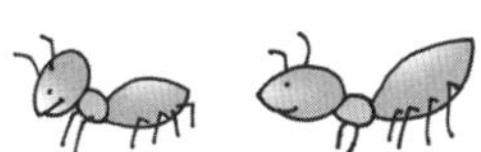

PHOTO FINISH!

Here's a mystery picture for you to identify. Just draw what you see in each of the numbered boxes into the blank boxes which have the same number on the opposite page.

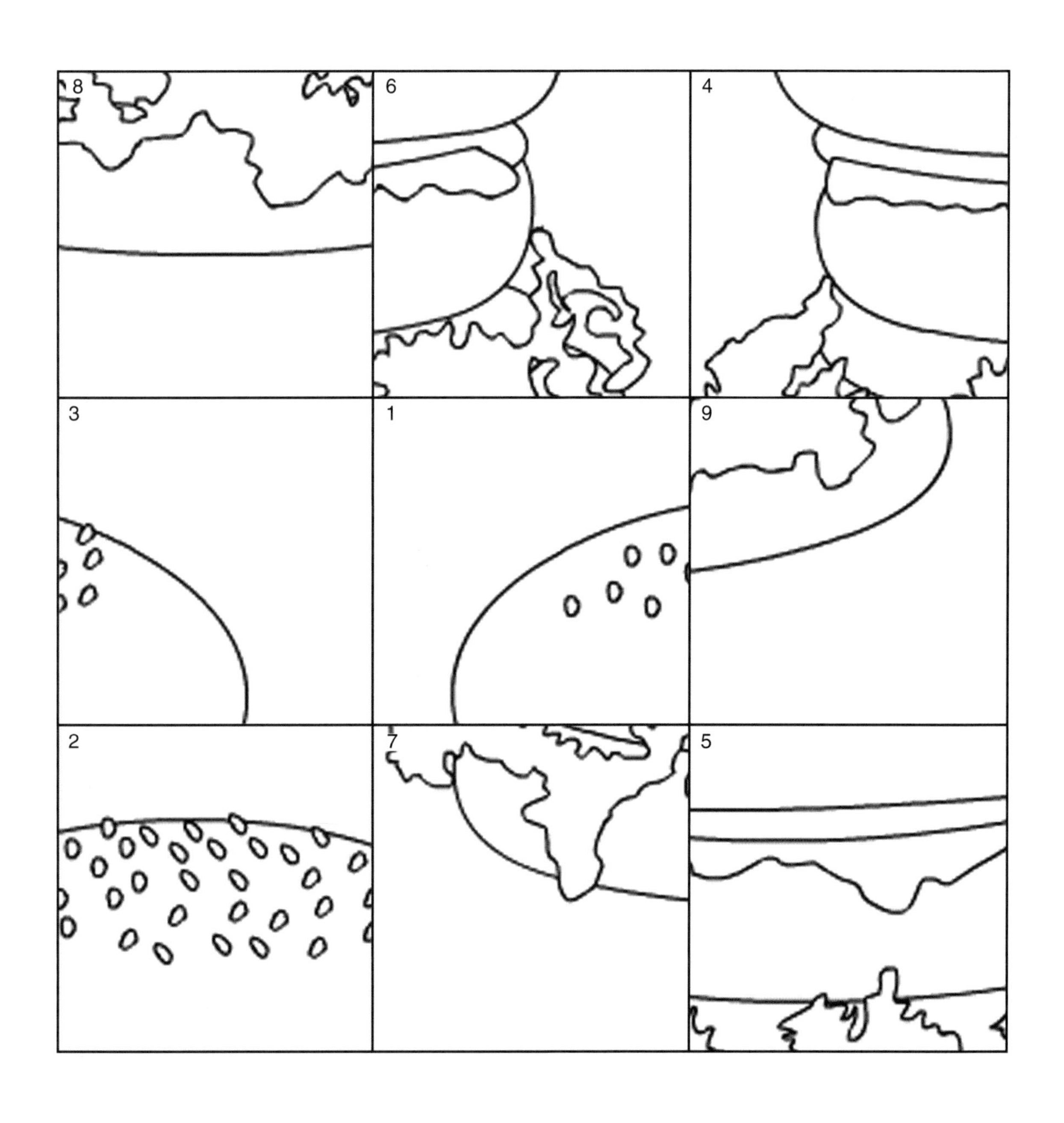

1	2	3
4	5	6
7	8	9

FOLLOW THE LEAD!

These letters make a word when they are put in the right order.
Track each letter along its path and then write
it in its correct place to find out what the word is.

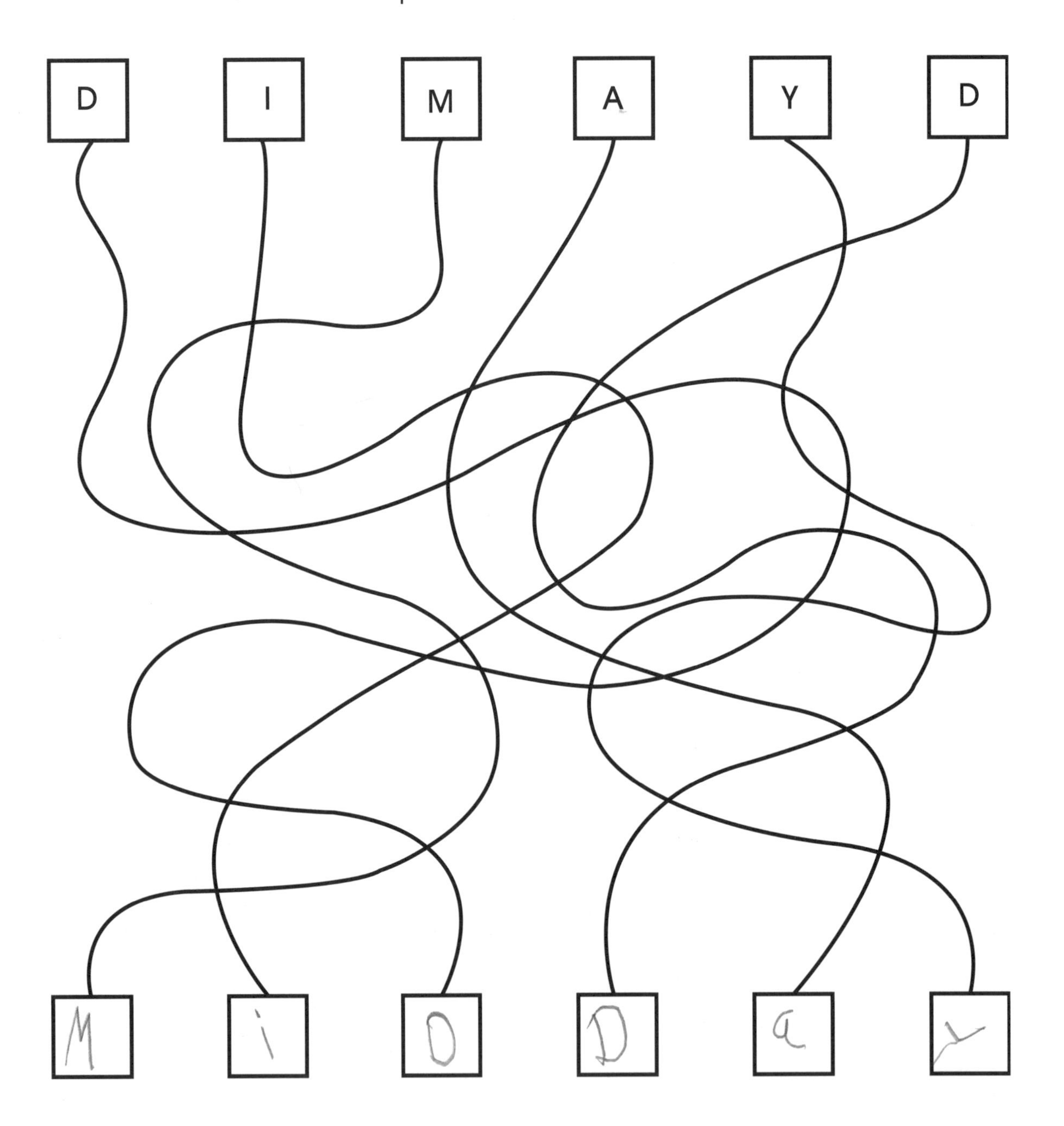

ROYAL MOUNTS!

Black horses and riders going right or white horses and riders going left?
Which way do you think the kings are headed?

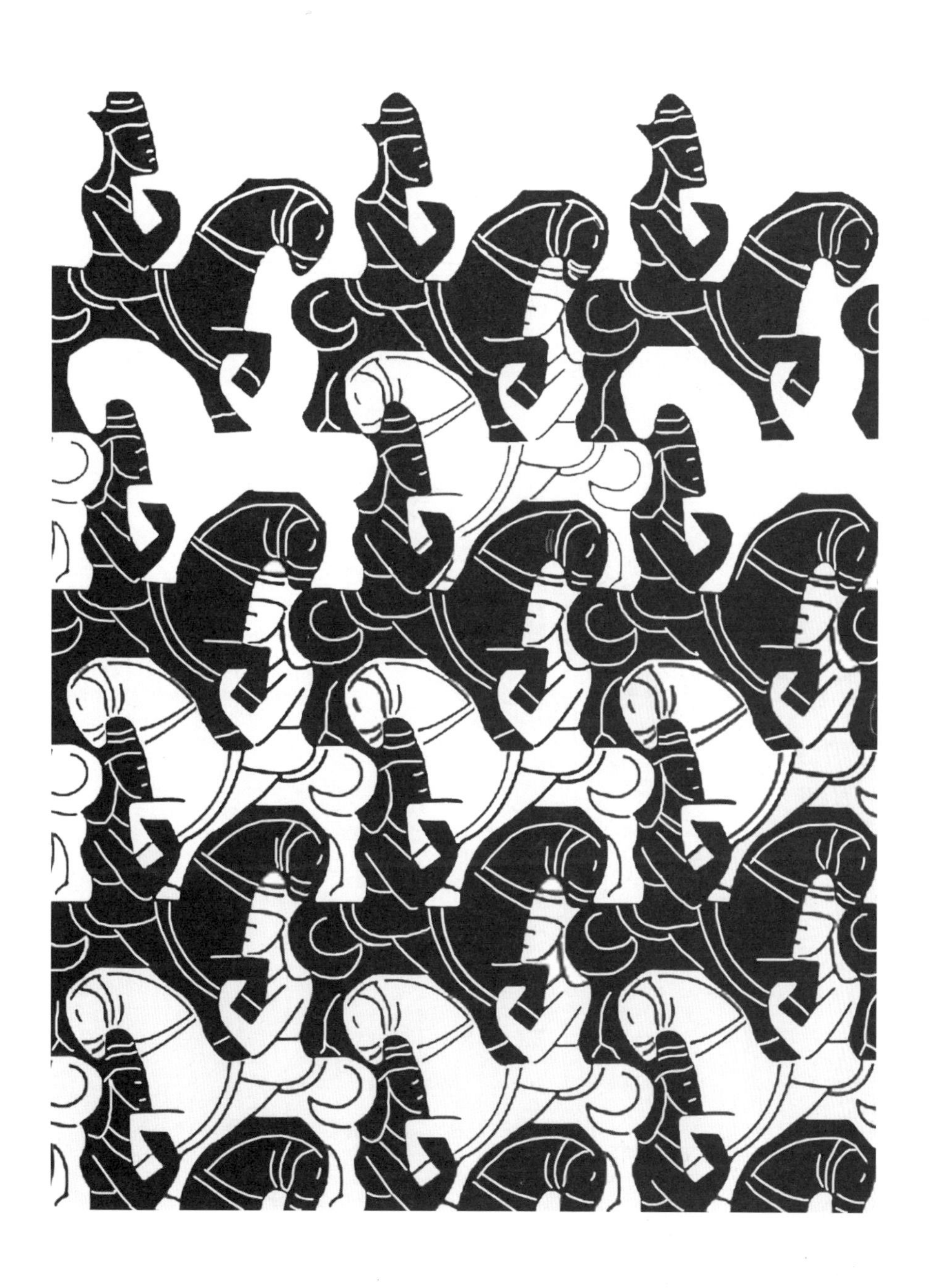

HONK! HONK!

The school bus will be here any moment now. Before it comes, look at the list of objects below and then find them in this picture.

Ballerina

Bulb

Cheese

Computer

Giraffe

Glass of water

Olympic rings

Parachute

Telephone receiver

Tie

PiX MiX!

How good are you at reading pictures?
You had better be good! Use the visual hints to correctly fill in the words in this picture crossword.

Across

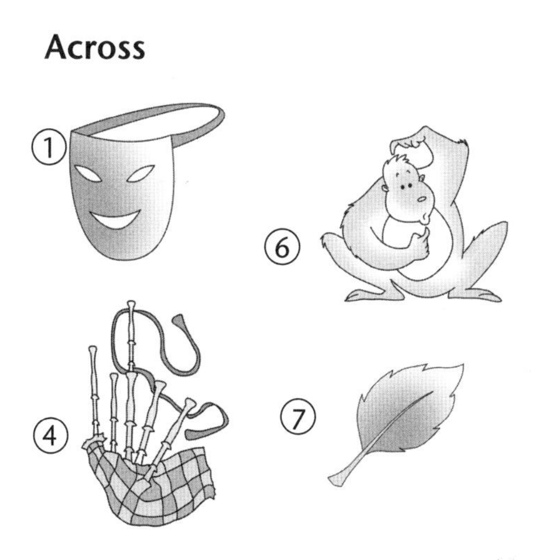

Down

CLONE CLOWNS!

There are two identical clowns in this group.
Look carefully and draw a circle around the two that are exactly the same.

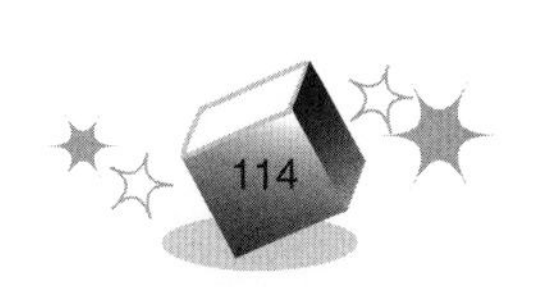

MAKE SENSE!

The first and last letters of some five letter words are given below.
How many can you think of?
To start you off, the first word could be MOVIE.

_ _ _

M _ _ _ E
M _ _ _ E
M _ _ _ E
M _ _ _ E
M _ _ _ E
M _ _ _ E
M _ _ _ E
M _ _ _ E
M _ _ _ E
M _ _ _ E
M _ _ _ E

Good: 1 – 4
V. Good: 5 – 8
Excellent: 9 – 12

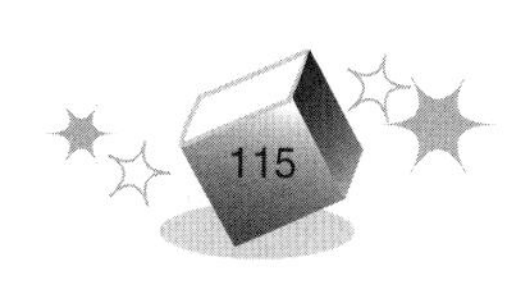

FLOWER POWER!

Let's make a special bouquet! Look at the list below and find and circle all the flowers in this word grid. (*Hint - Look up, down, across and diagonally*)

E	S	T	G	E	L	Y	C	N	W	L	U	M	D	M
I	J	U	G	K	T	S	G	M	P	G	U	C	A	A
C	S	A	N	P	L	O	L	O	Y	M	T	C	F	I
P	E	S	V	F	R	G	V	A	E	N	I	R	F	D
M	S	B	V	C	L	F	M	H	Z	K	K	X	O	S
O	V	I	H	V	Q	O	T	P	G	U	W	Y	D	J
W	L	I	Z	F	X	N	W	X	Y	M	Z	D	I	C
X	D	I	E	O	A	T	C	E	I	Z	O	V	L	B
E	W	S	K	S	Y	B	T	J	R	N	C	S	R	P
R	O	R	Y	G	G	X	E	E	O	Y	G	W	E	K
R	E	R	T	E	L	O	I	V	U	J	S	A	T	K
B	H	A	P	E	L	A	P	S	Q	E	C	I	S	D
C	Q	O	B	C	A	R	N	A	T	I	O	N	A	K
L	I	L	Y	Y	U	G	L	V	Z	C	W	D	X	D
E	H	Y	E	K	S	Y	Z	E	I	P	R	Z	F	C

ASTER
DAFFODIL
ORCHID
VIOLET

CARNATION
DAISY
ROSE

CHRYSANTHEMUM
LILY
SUNFLOWER

SCIENCE CLASS!

Can you remember all that you see? Well, let's find out!
Study this picture carefully and then turn the page to answer some questions.
No peeking back at this page though!

QUESTIONS

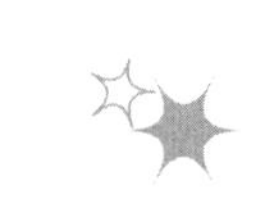

1. Are the children all wearing white coats?
2. Is there a broken beaker?
3. Is the science teacher watching over the children?
4. What is in the big glass jar?
5. How many microscopes are there?
6. Are there any frogs around?
7. How many children are writing in their notebooks?
8. Where is the smoke coming from?
9. Is there a genie?
10. What is written on the board?

BUILD IT UP!

Starting from the top, move down each step adding one letter as you go then rearrange all the letters around the 'S' to make a new word every time.

Here's a mystery picture for you to identify. Just draw what you see in each of the numbered boxes into the blank boxes which have the same number on the opposite page.

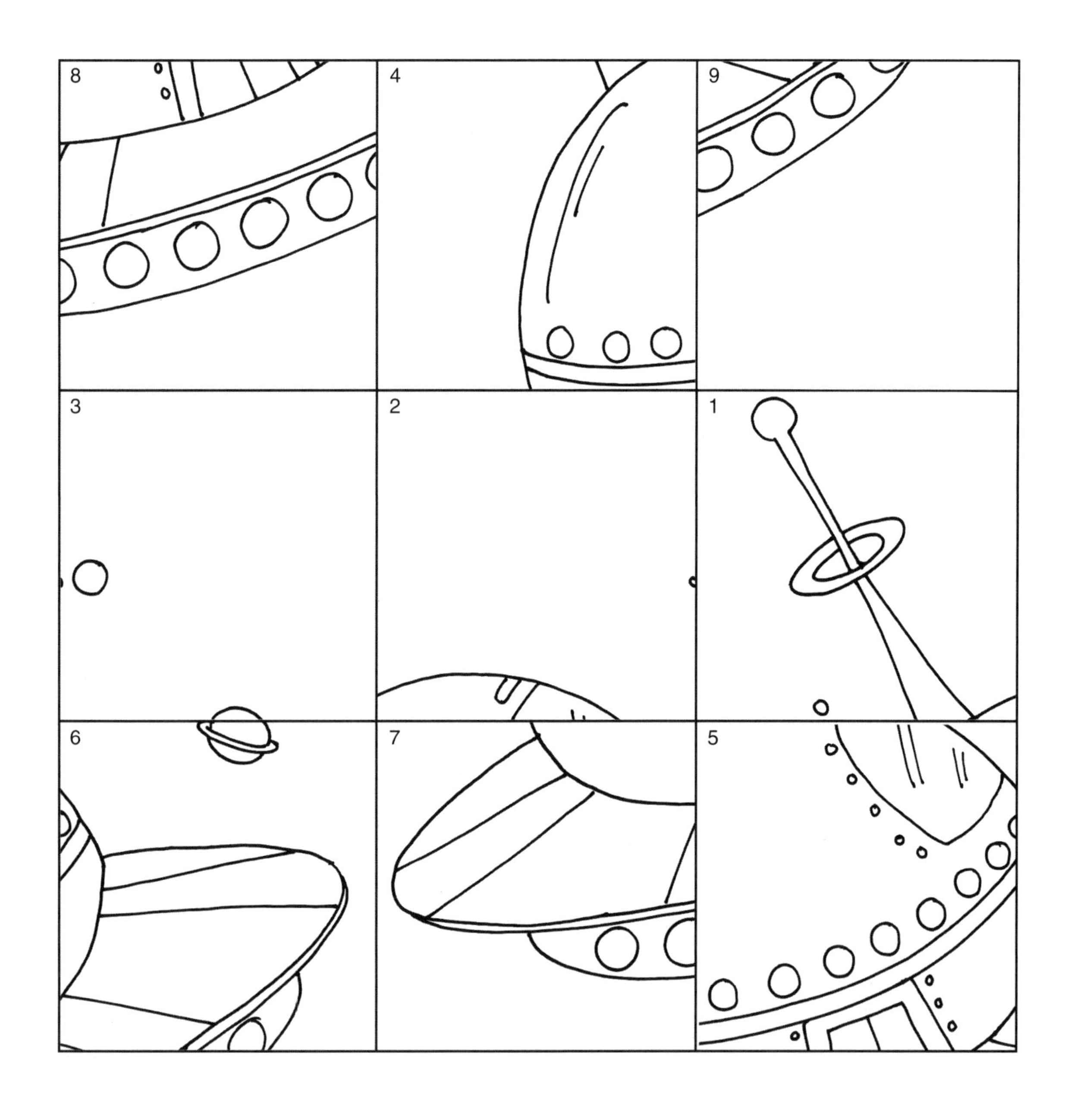

1	2	3
4	5	6
7	8	9

WHAT'S IT SAY?

These letters make a word when they are put in the right order.
Track each letter along its path and then write it in its
correct place to find out what the word is.

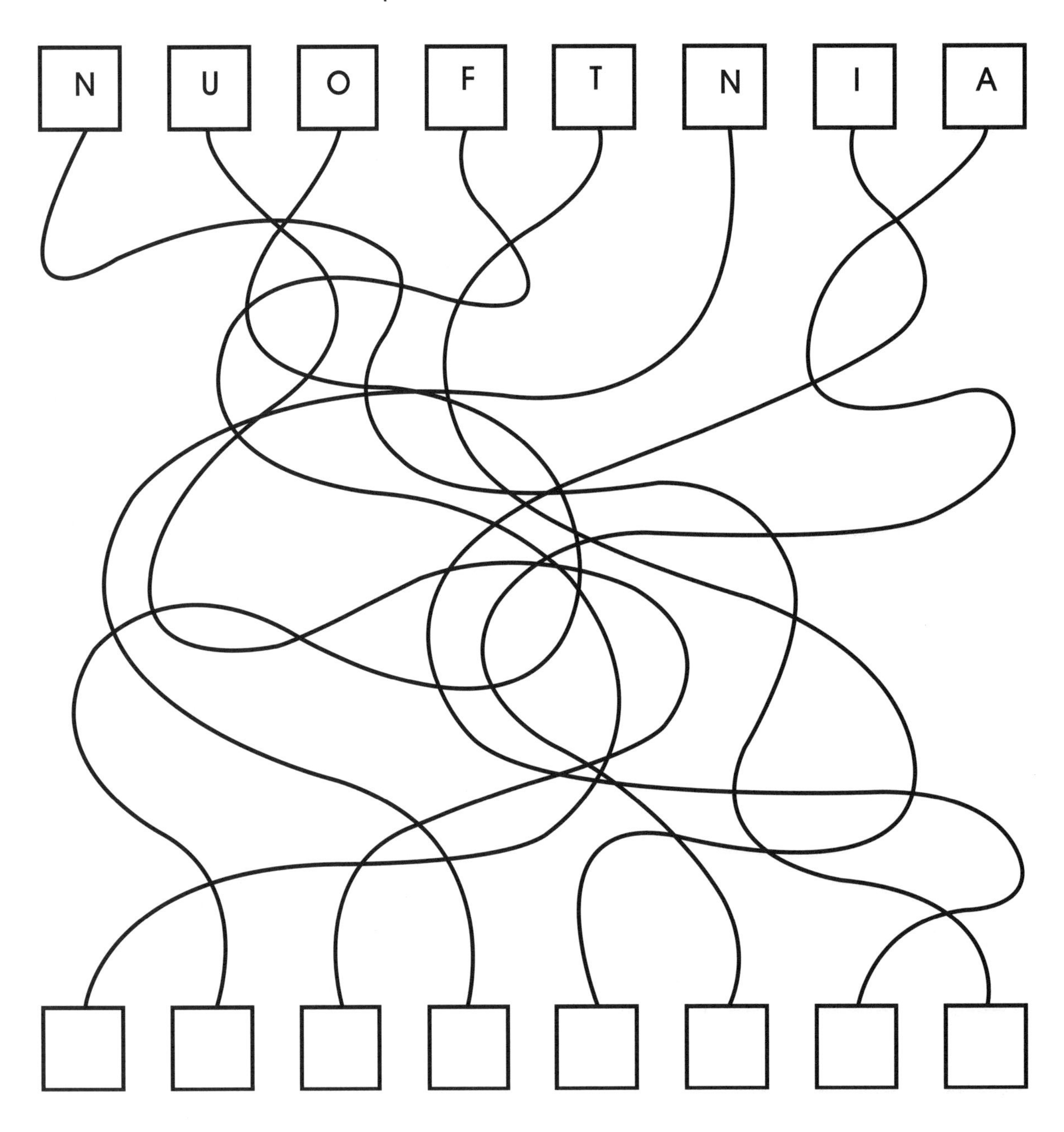

SQUARE FARE!

Do you think this square has straight lines or are the lines warped?
If you look carefully you will be able to make it out.

ZOO-OLOGY!

Do you like going to the zoo? Look at the list below then see if you can find the objects hidden in this picture.

Bear

Boy in baseball cap

Cheetah

Crow

Fan blades

Gloves

Loaf of bread

Man wearing mask

Squirrel

Tripod

PICTURE PUZZLER!

How good are you at reading pictures? You had better be good! Use the visual hints to correctly fill in the words in this picture crossword.

Across

③ 

⑦ 

Down

① 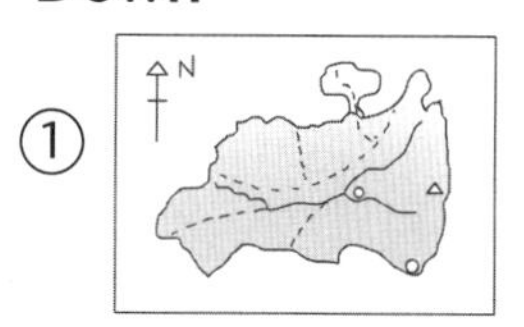

⑤ 

② 

⑥ 

④ 

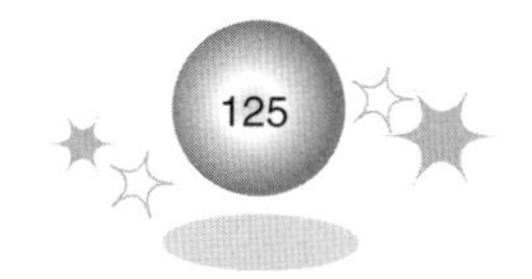

HELLO?!

We need two identical cellphones.
Look carefully at this group then draw a circle around the two that are exactly the same.

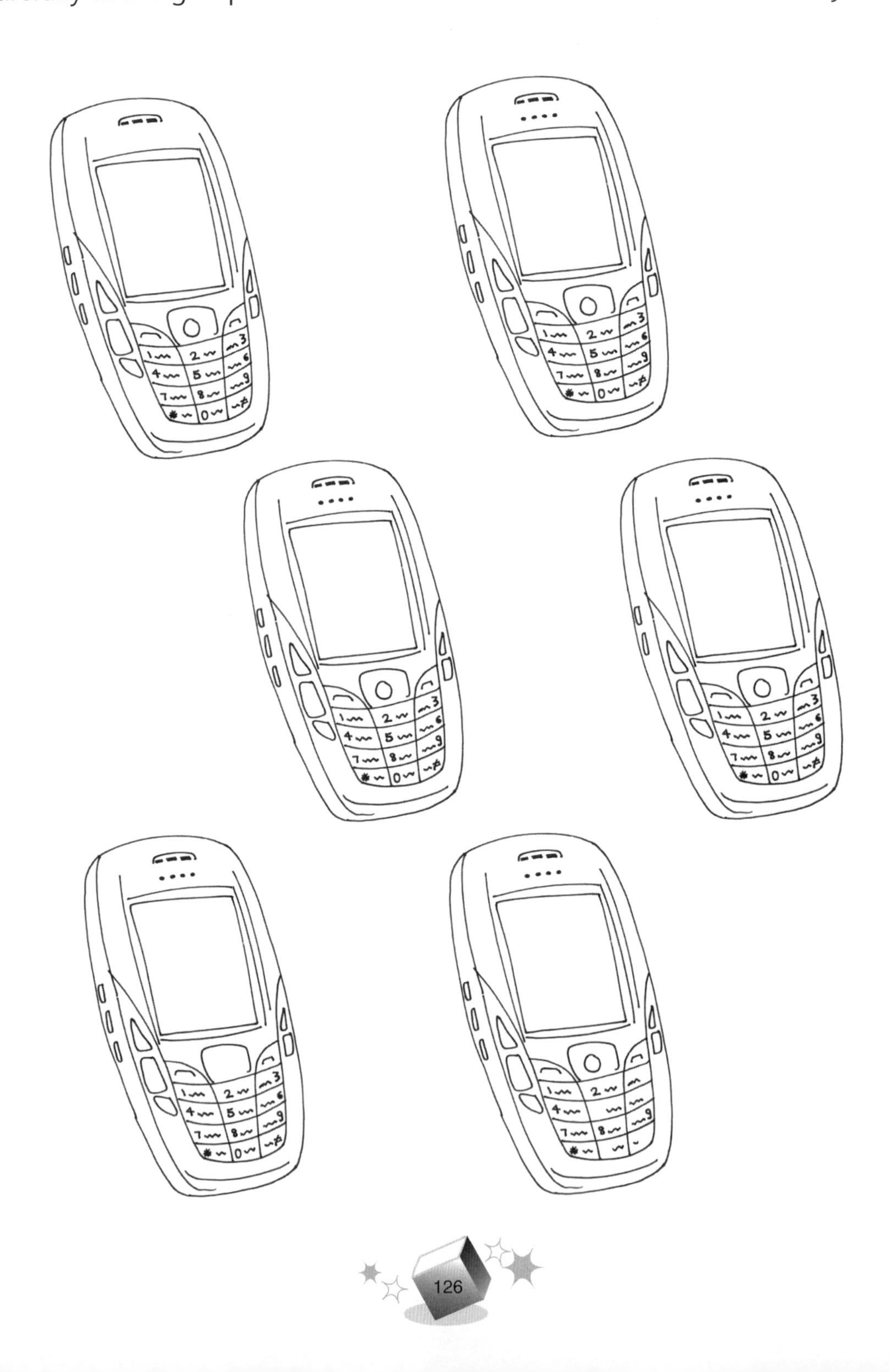

CENTRAL CRISIS!

The first and last letters of some five letter words are given below. How many can you think of?
To start you off, the first word could be ROBOT.

R _ _ _ T

R _ _ _ T

R _ _ _ T

R _ _ _ T

R _ _ _ T

Good:	1 – 2
V. Good:	3
Excellent:	4 – 5

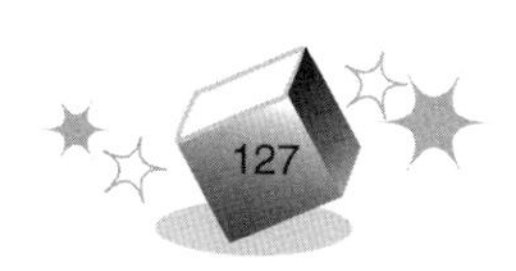

10 DOWNING STREET!

Can you name some of the residents of this esteemed address?
Look at the list of Prime Ministers, then find and circle them in this word grid.
(Hint -Look up, down, across and diagonally)

N	D	D	H	E	H	U	C	M	L	N	R	Z	N	J
O	Q	W	T	T	Q	Z	B	X	E	M	Y	I	V	O
S	N	Z	S	O	E	U	M	D	S	C	W	V	G	H
L	Q	P	N	U	N	T	E	J	A	D	E	G	E	N
I	B	Z	Z	U	H	Y	H	H	L	G	S	W	N	M
W	E	O	S	B	N	J	B	A	L	W	M	U	P	A
D	K	B	Q	O	N	R	B	L	J	R	T	W	K	J
L	D	Z	H	R	N	Y	G	K	A	L	I	Q	F	O
O	K	T	T	Q	E	L	C	S	Y	I	E	F	R	R
R	N	L	S	L	P	Q	L	H	N	J	R	A	R	F
A	U	Q	N	E	D	W	A	R	D	H	E	A	T	H
H	J	A	N	D	R	E	W	L	A	W	N	R	L	D
P	T	O	T	B	T	E	Y	M	N	R	D	A	V	E
S	N	A	H	G	A	L	L	A	C	S	E	M	A	J
O	E	E	A	T	W	Y	W	H	K	Z	W	E	E	M

ANTHONY EDEN
JAMES CALLAGHAN
STANLEY BALDWIN
EDWARD HEATH
ANDREW LAW
TONY BLAIR
HAROLD WILSON
JOHN MAJOR

DINNER'S READY!

Can you remember all that you see? Well, let's find out!
Study this picture carefully and then turn the page to answer some questions.
No peeking back at this page though!

QUESTIONS

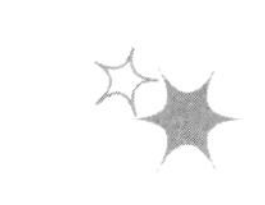

1. What's for dinner?
2. How many people is the table laid for?
3. Are the candles lit?
4. Is there a wine bottle?
5. Does the table cloth have little hearts or flowers printed on it?
6. Is the bread basket filled?
7. Has the soup already been served?
8. Are there stars in the sky?
9. Is there fruit?
10. What ice-cream is there for dessert?

ADD AND ENJOY!

Starting from the top, move down each step adding one letter as you go then rearrange all the letters around the 'H' to make a new word every time.

FROM DOWN UNDER!

Here's a mystery picture for you to identify. Just draw what you see in each of the numbered boxes into the blank boxes which have the same number on the opposite page.

1	2	3
4	5	6
7	8	9

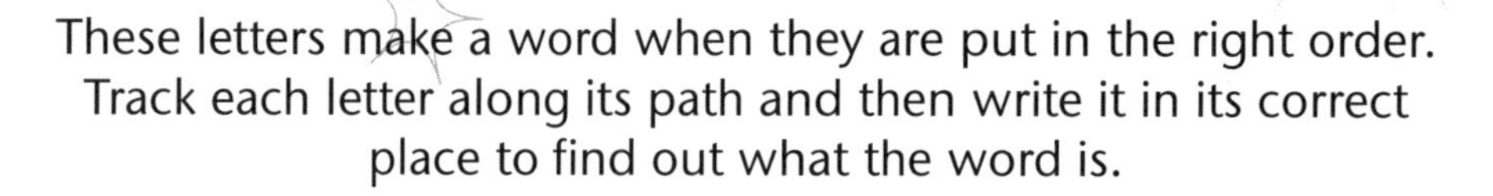

These letters make a word when they are put in the right order. Track each letter along its path and then write it in its correct place to find out what the word is.

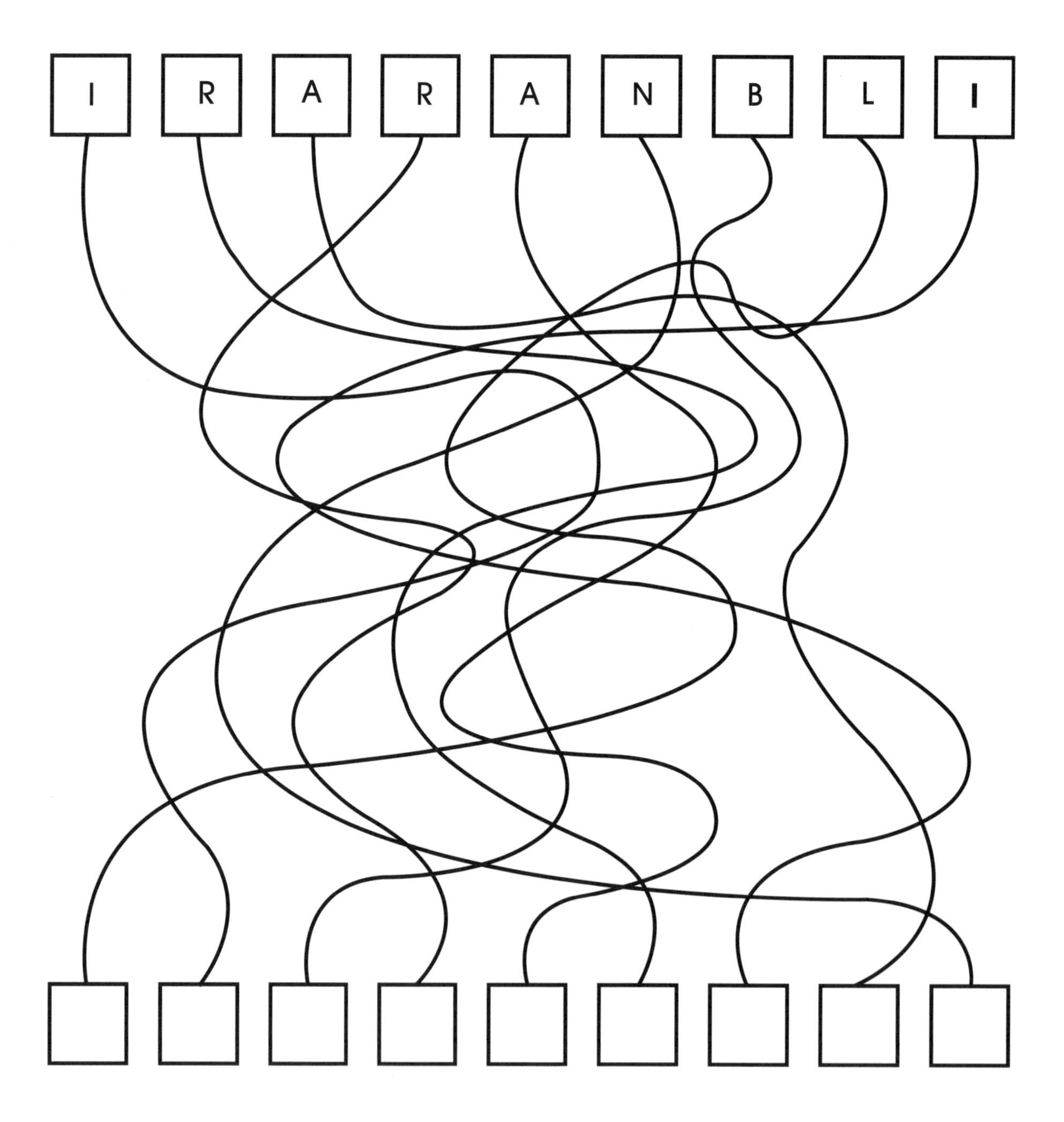

MUSICIAN OR MUSE?

Do you see a musician, a lady's face or do you see both?
Rub your eyes and look again to clear the mystery.

SNOW FUN!

The snow has covered everything up!
Can you look for all the objects in the list below that are hidden in this picture?

Candle
Candy cane
Comb
Christmas tree
Duck
Mittens
Paw print
Puppy
Sheep
Sundae

PICTURE THIS!

How good are you at reading pictures?
You had better be good!
Use the visual hints to correctly fill in the words in this picture crossword.

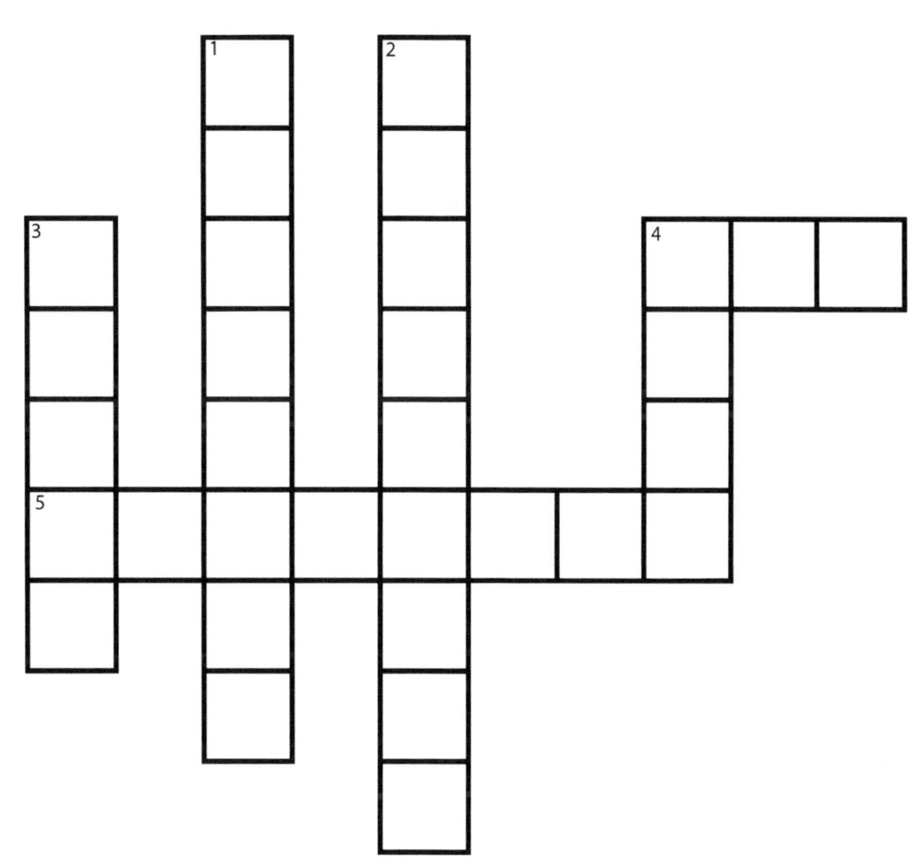

Across

4
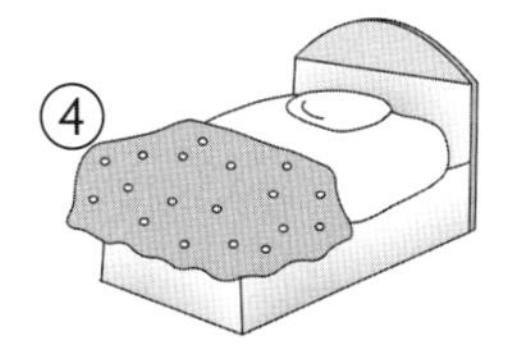

5

Down

DUCKIE DUOS!

There are two identical ducks in this group.
Look carefully and draw a circle around the two that are exactly the same.

AT THE CORE!

The first and last letters of some five letter words are given below.
How many can you think of? To start you off, the first word could be LASER.

L _ _ _ R

L _ _ _ R

L _ _ _ R

L _ _ _ R

L _ _ _ R

L _ _ _ R

L _ _ _ R

L _ _ _ R

L _ _ _ R

L _ _ _ R

Good:	1 – 5
V. Good:	6 – 7
Excellent:	8 – 10

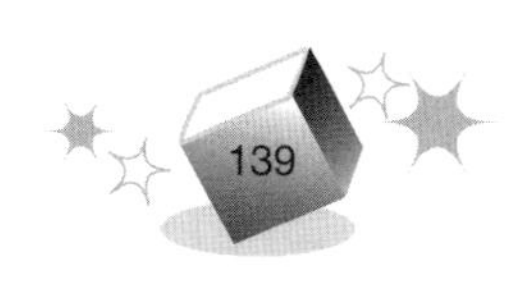

FRUIT FLAVOURS!

What a healthy snack! Here's a list of fruits for you to look up so that you can find and circle them all in this word grid. (*Hint - Look up, down, across and diagonally*)

W	E	X	H	Z	G	N	E	B	T	U	P	O	Q	Q
P	I	N	E	A	P	P	L	E	A	S	A	F	G	V
N	E	G	N	A	R	O	P	W	Q	N	P	R	T	N
O	E	L	Y	I	I	J	P	T	A	B	A	X	G	O
L	S	P	P	M	B	U	A	S	H	P	Y	N	K	Y
E	F	M	J	P	S	C	D	I	E	L	A	S	A	Y
M	L	H	S	X	A	I	R	S	V	W	C	X	R	O
V	U	X	F	X	U	T	A	A	N	H	O	R	G	S
L	V	L	B	T	F	O	T	E	H	A	E	N	B	A
P	S	I	H	Z	K	Z	S	N	A	B	A	M	O	R
C	V	F	W	H	C	U	U	D	W	M	S	I	A	X
O	T	A	D	B	V	G	C	A	H	F	Q	H	F	Y
L	E	D	O	L	Z	N	R	G	Z	N	K	E	V	M
N	L	R	K	L	N	T	B	P	D	Z	K	O	M	I
I	F	M	A	I	S	Y	F	D	L	M	J	T	L	F

APPLE
BANANA
CUSTARD APPLE
GRAPES
MANGO
MELON
ORANGE
PAPAYA
PINEAPPLE
STRAWBERRY

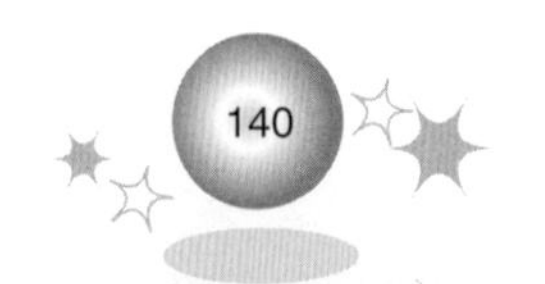

ONCE UPON A TIME!

Can you remember all that you see? Well, let's find out! Study this picture carefully and then turn the page to answer some questions. No peeking back at this page though!

QUESTIONS

1. How many children are there?
2. Who is reading from the story book?
3. What prints are there on the little boy's pajamas?
4. How many kites are there?
5. Which bird can be seen from the window?
6. Is there a cat in the picture?
7. Who is sleeping?
8. Is the jug of water covered with a saucer?
9. What time is the clock showing?
10. Where is the teddy bear?

WORD BRICKS!

Starting from the top, move down each step adding one letter as you go then rearrange all the letters around the 'R' to make a new word every time.

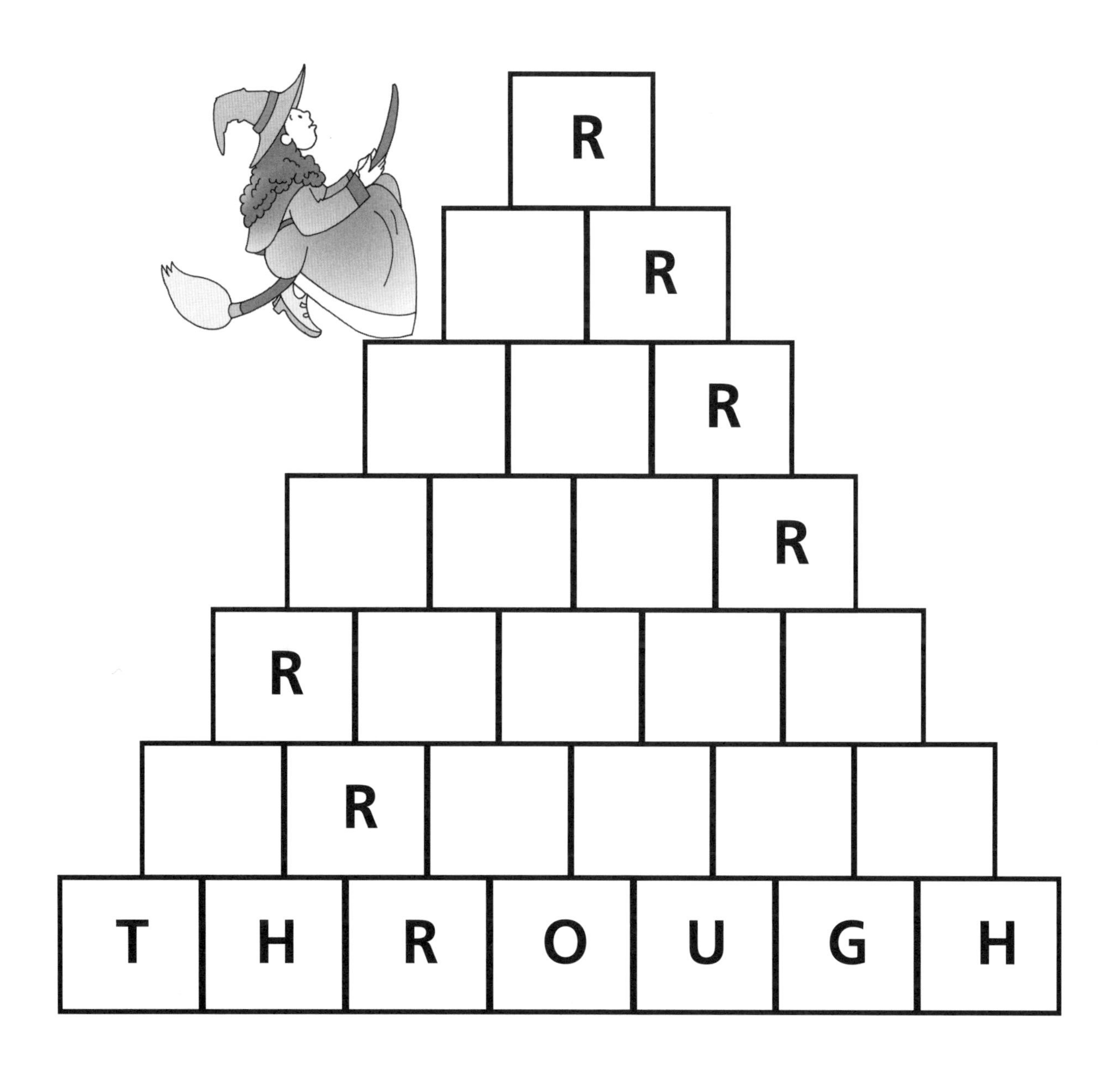

Here's a mystery picture for you to identify. Just draw what you see in each of the numbered boxes into the blank boxes which have the same number on the opposite page.

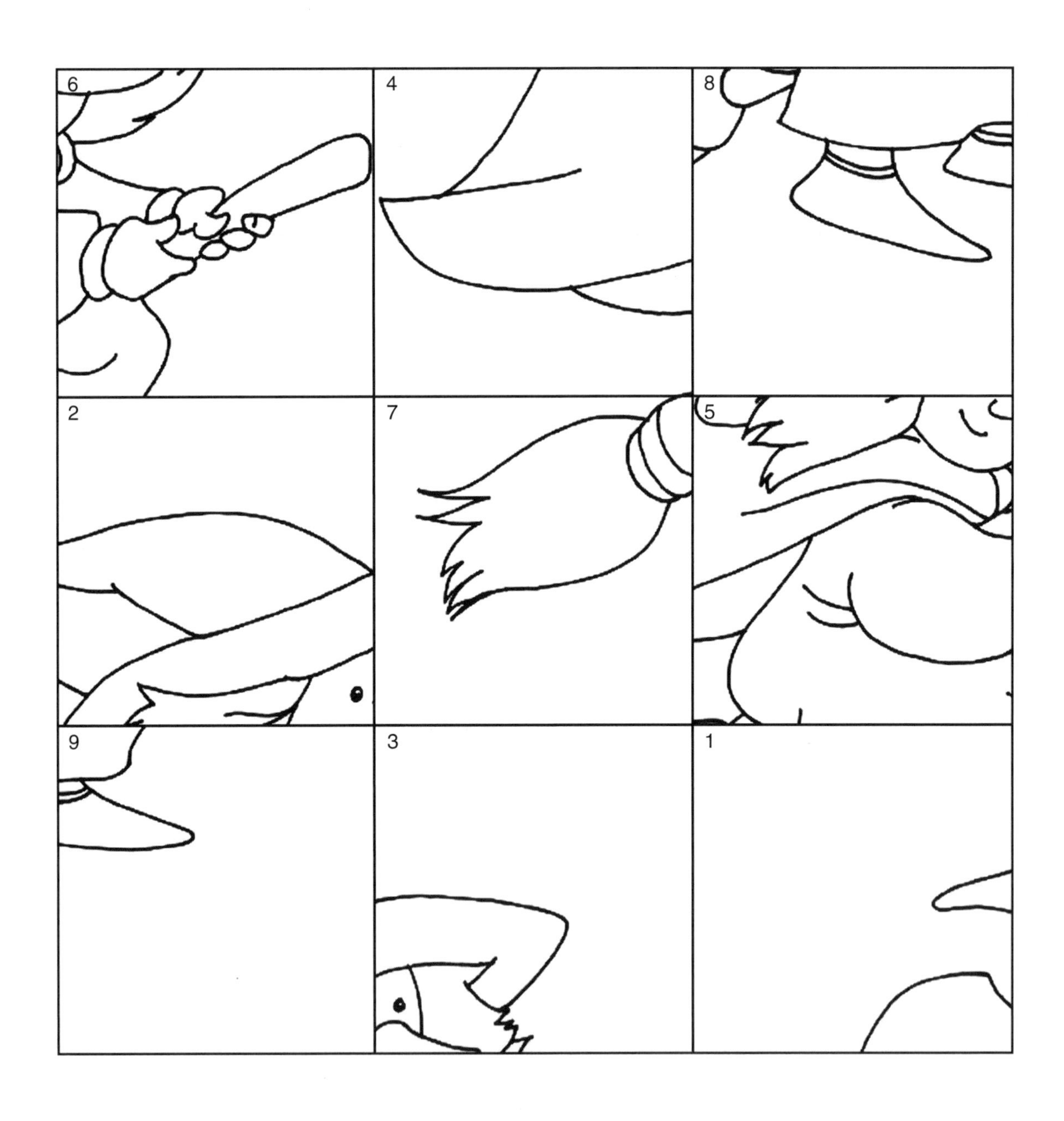

1	2	3
4	5	6
7	8	9

MAZE FROM MARS!

These letters make a word when they are put in the right order. Track each letter along its path and then write it in its correct place to find out what the word is.

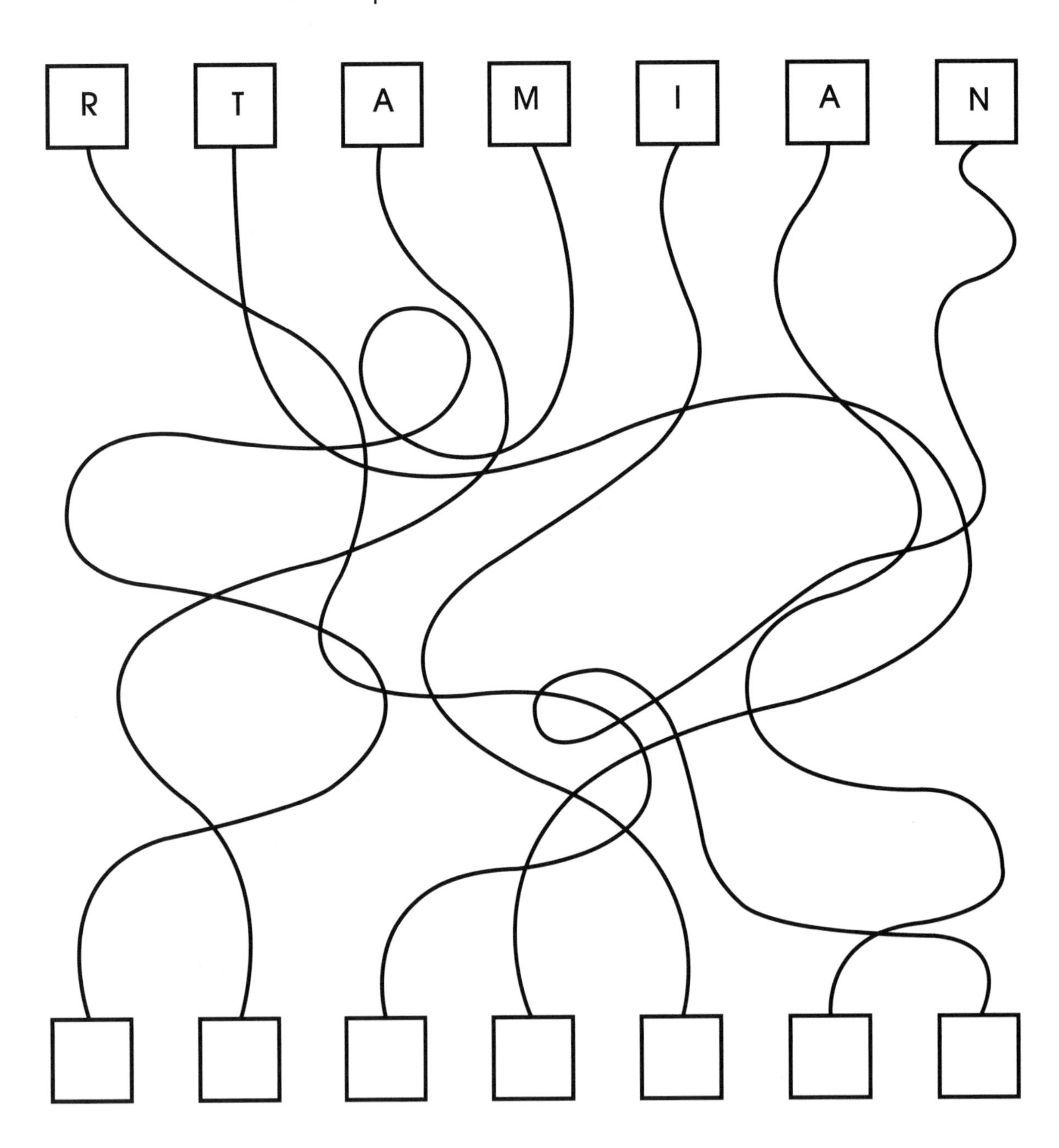

STANDING TALL!

Is this a picture of a balcony or is it some women standing up?
Can you figure out this optical illusion?

DENTAL iMAGE!

This won't hurt at all! All you have to do is look for all the objects listed below that are hidden in this picture.

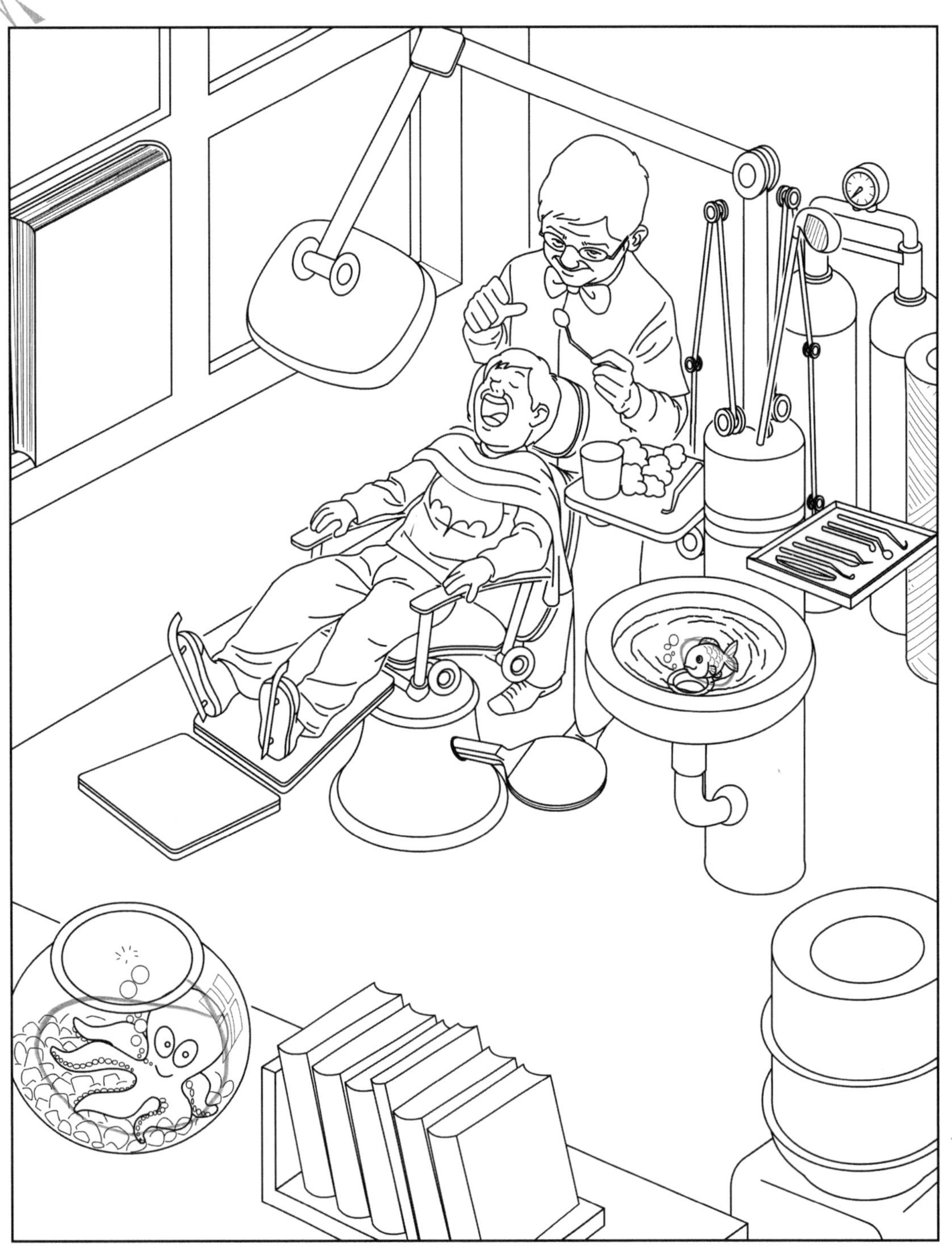

Bat

Book

Bow-tie

Cotton wool

Gold fish

Golf clubs

Ice-skates

Octopus

Spindle of yarn

Table tennis bat

FIX THE PIX!

How good are you at reading pictures?
You had better be good! Use the visual hints to
correctly fill in the words in this picture crossword.

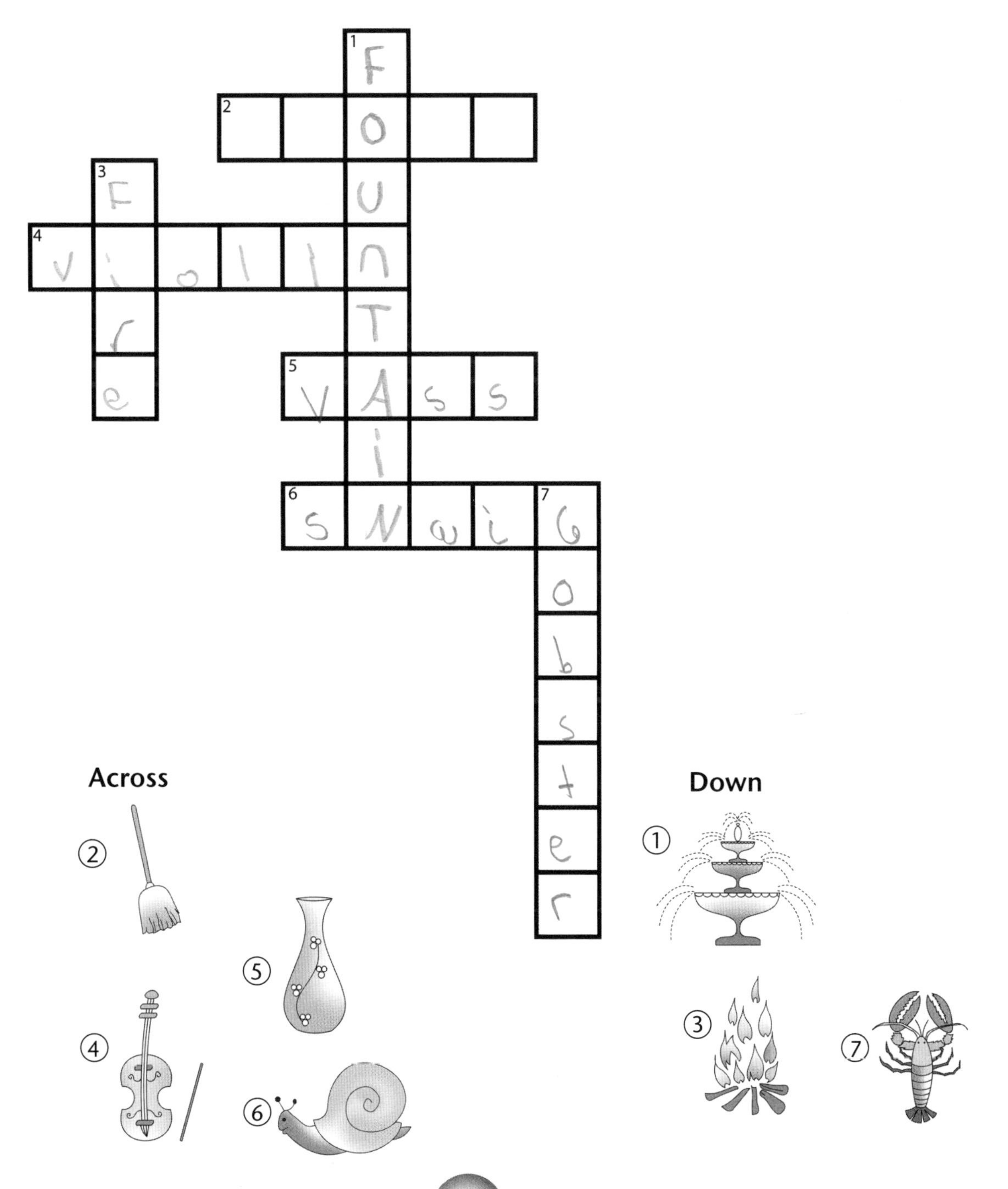

DOUBLE BEATS!

There are two identical drums in this group.
Look carefully and draw a circle around the two that are exactly the same.

MISSING MIDDLES!

The first and last letters of some five letter words are given below.
How many can you think of?
To start you off, the first word could be NIECE.

N _ _ _ E

N _ _ _ E

N _ _ _ E

N _ _ _ E

N _ _ _ E

☺ Good: 1 – 2

☺ V. Good: 3

☺ Excellent: 4 – 5

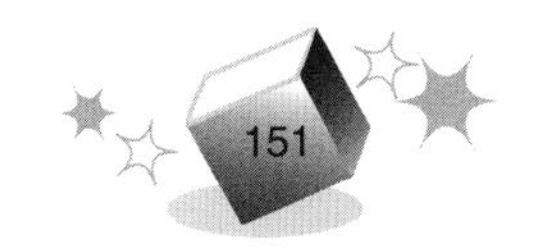

WANT TO PLAY?

Are you a real sport? How about looking at this sports list and searching this word grid for all of them? (*Hint - Look up, down, across and diagonally*)

S	Y	B	X	U	C	X	A	A	N	A	L	J	B	V
X	I	Y	A	V	I	P	Z	O	V	C	L	C	C	X
C	W	N	V	S	T	U	T	H	Y	W	A	E	Y	Q
B	X	Y	N	E	E	N	H	F	I	Y	B	N	L	O
C	Z	B	N	E	I	B	O	A	B	B	T	C	A	D
J	P	N	B	M	T	L	A	O	S	G	E	R	V	U
F	I	I	D	O	O	E	H	L	F	U	K	I	G	P
S	C	A	S	P	P	J	L	S	L	R	S	C	O	J
Y	B	G	N	I	X	O	B	B	A	K	A	K	D	T
F	O	O	T	B	A	L	L	V	A	U	B	E	F	Z
R	R	X	E	L	U	S	S	E	V	T	Q	T	H	F
K	C	N	L	E	V	Q	I	W	S	K	G	S	W	S
P	I	B	G	V	E	T	L	Q	A	W	R	O	P	F
M	V	Y	F	Q	Z	U	V	K	B	U	Q	E	R	L
E	F	T	V	R	Y	Z	B	Z	Z	G	N	O	Z	L

BADMINTON
BOXING
POLO
TABLE TENNIS

BASEBALL
CRICKET
RUGBY
TENNIS

BASKETBALL
FOOTBALL
SQUASH

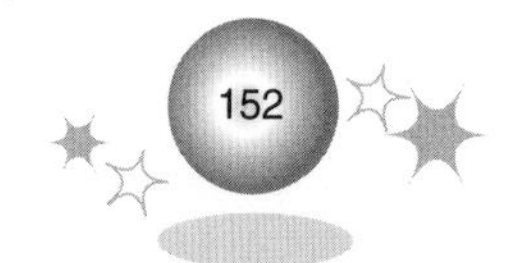

SCRUB! SCRUB! SCRUB!

Can you remember all that you see? Well, let's find out! Study this picture carefully and then turn the page to answer some questions. No peeking back at this page though!

QUESTIONS

1. Are the baskets circular or rectangular?
2. Is the washing machine on?
3. What is written on the detergent carton?
4. Is there a dryer?
5. Who has curled up on the washed clothes?
6. How many fabric softener bottles are there?
7. Is there a separate basket for the woolens?
8. Is the radio playing a song?
9. What is the woman doing?
10. Is the little boy wearing a sweater?

FROM ONE TO SEVEN!

Starting from the top, move down each step adding one letter as you go then rearrange all the letters around the 'S' to make a new word every time.

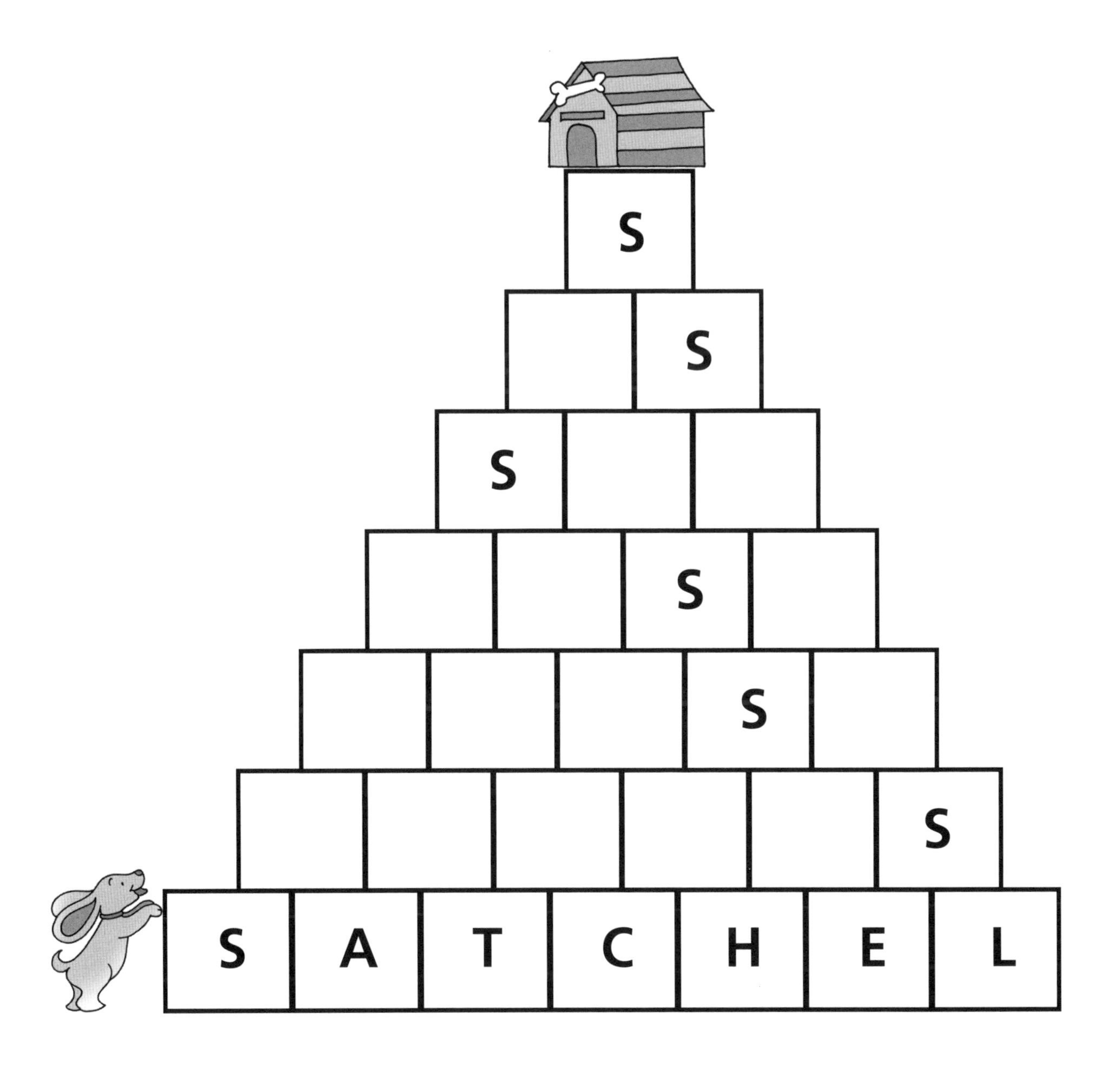

DRAW AND TELL!

Here's a mystery picture for you to identify. Just draw what you see in each of the numbered boxes into the blank boxes which have the same number on the opposite page.

1	2	3
4	5	6
7	8	9

A-MAZE-MENT!

These letters make a word when they are put in the right order. Track each letter along its path and then write it in its correct place to find out what the word is.

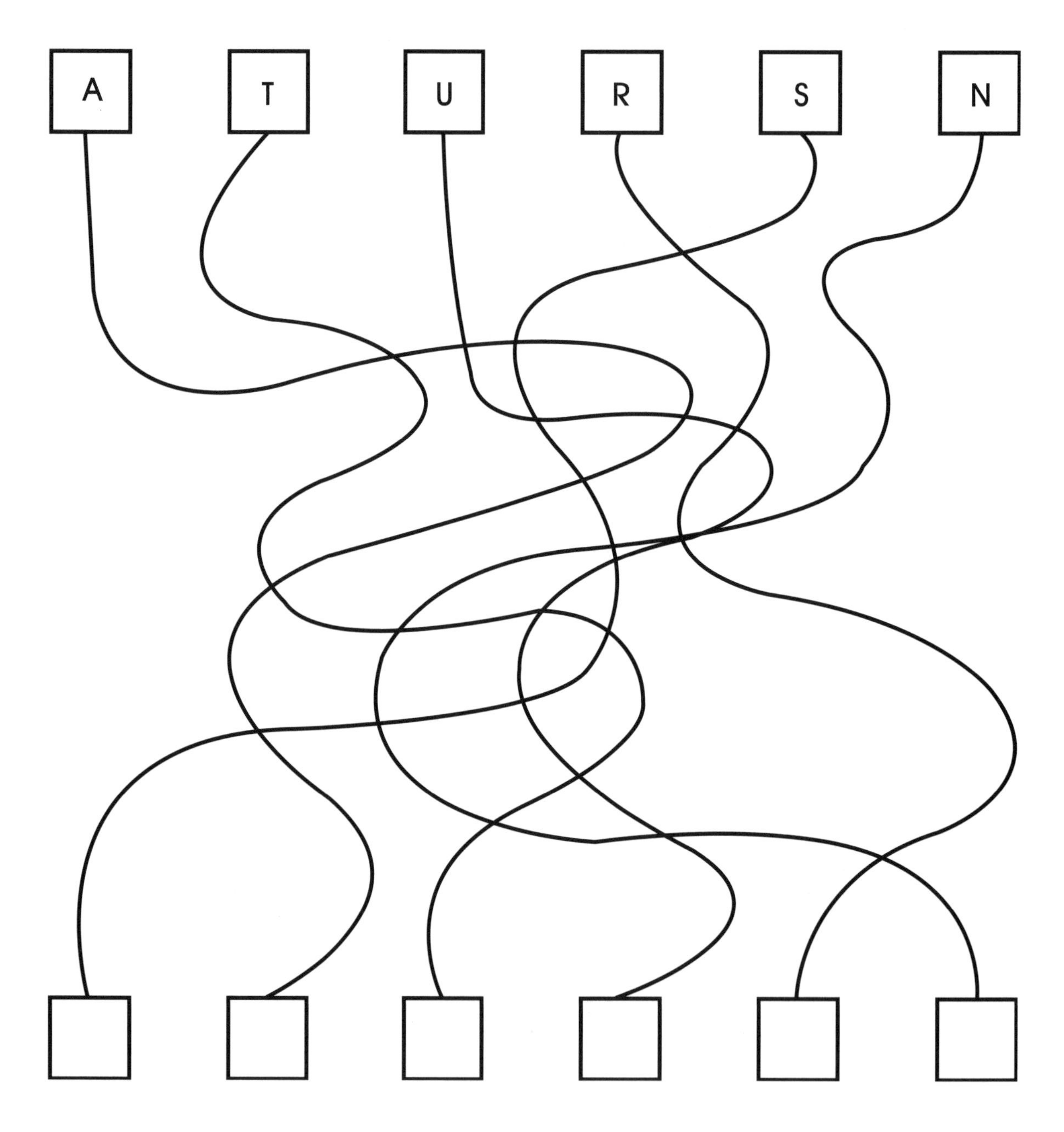

BOOK BLUNDER!

What's wrong with this book? Is it facing down or is it facing up?
You will need to look really hard to try and figure this one out!

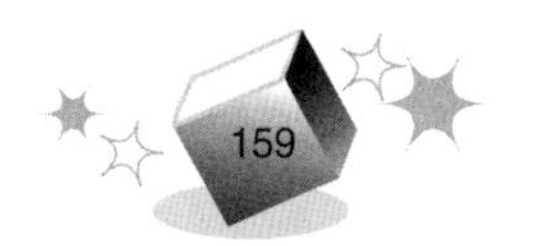

SOMETHING FISHY!

Here's a fish tank that needs your full attention.
Can you look for all the objects listed below that are hidden in this picture?

Eel
Flippers
Igloo
Key
Ship mast
Star
Measuring
tape
Rose
String of pearls
Tea cup

FLYING HIGH!

How well do you know our feathery friends? Solve these visual clues to correctly fill in the bird names in this picture crossword.

PEAS IN A POD!

There are two identical pea pods in here.
Look carefully and draw a circle around the two that are exactly the same.

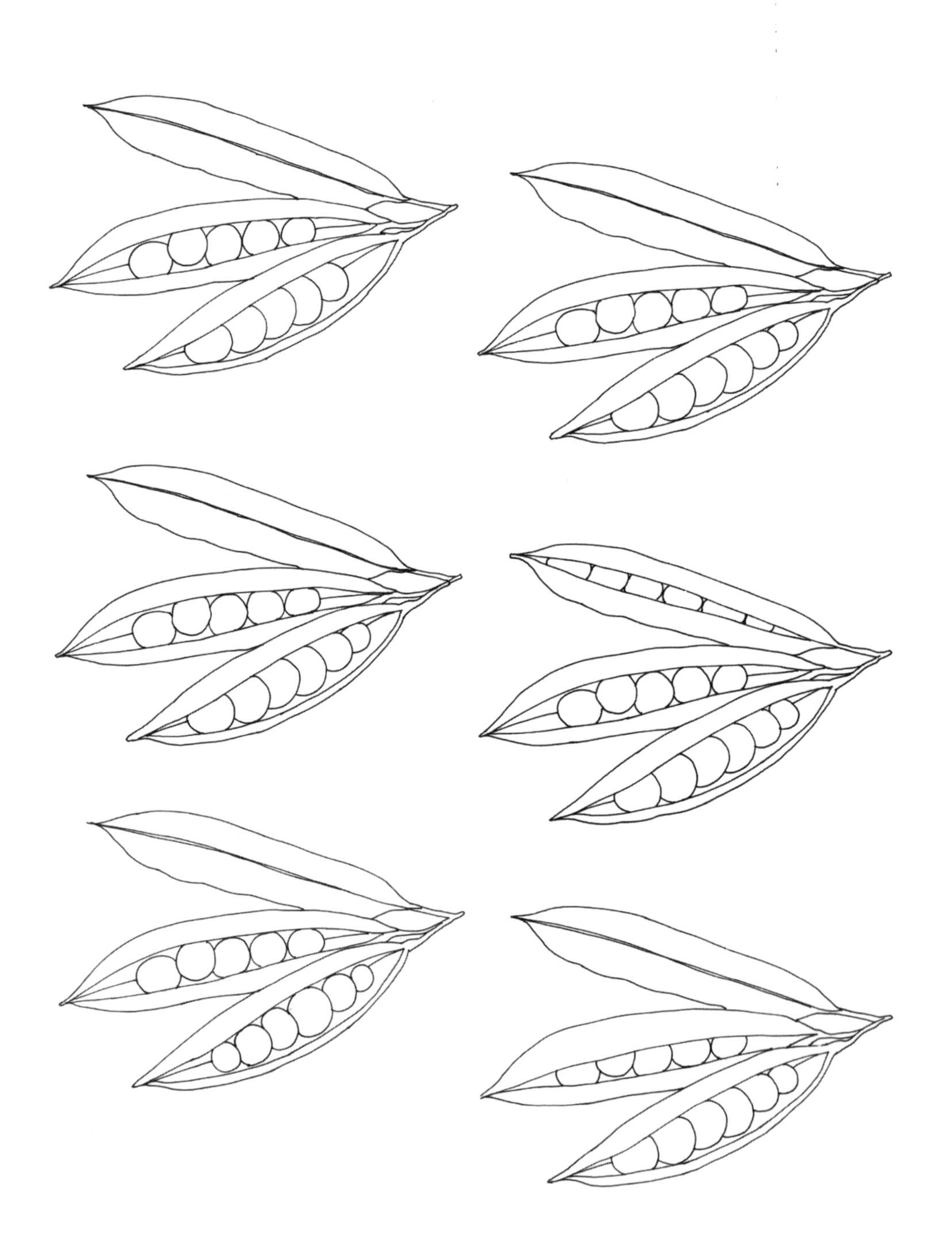

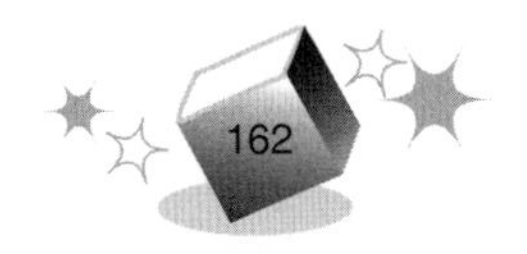

CORE PROBLEM!

The first and last letters of some five letter words are given below.
How many can you think of? To start you off, the first word could be WATCH.

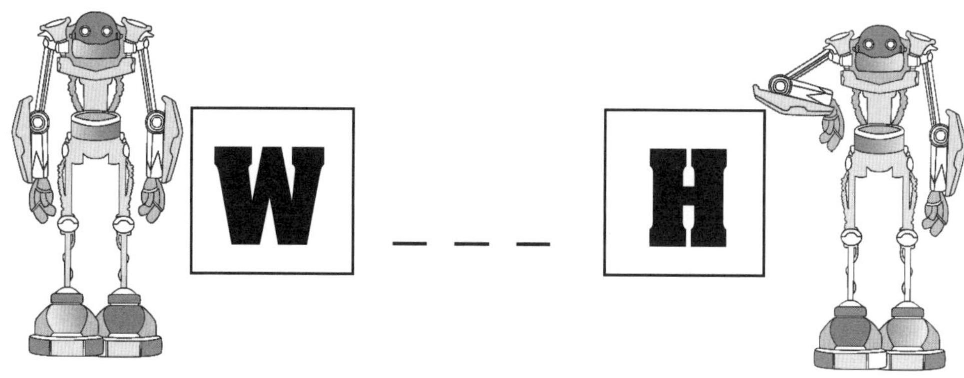

W _ _ _ H

W _ _ _ H

W _ _ _ H

W _ _ _ H

W _ _ _ H

W _ _ _ H

Good: 1 – 3

V. Good: 4 – 5

Excellent: 6 – 7

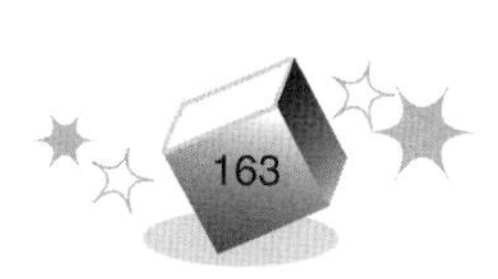

TRICK OR TREAT!

What comes to mind when someone says "Halloween"?
Here's a list of words that you might have thought of! Find and circle them all in this word grid.
(Hint - Look up, down, across and diagonally)

T	R	E	A	T	C	J	E	B	W	U	X	K	J	U
P	P	O	O	D	A	A	C	R	W	I	C	L	I	F
Q	U	Y	Q	Y	N	C	N	J	I	I	T	B	G	N
U	N	M	C	B	D	K	O	Q	R	P	R	C	K	I
H	N	W	P	R	Y	O	Z	T	L	O	M	K	H	L
Q	T	F	Z	K	H	L	Y	S	O	U	L	A	X	B
O	F	F	P	S	I	A	F	M	M	S	R	V	V	O
L	O	A	E	I	T	N	S	M	B	G	M	Y	S	G
G	O	V	M	M	M	T	P	K	Z	R	U	U	Y	R
R	V	A	B	W	I	E	O	A	D	Z	K	F	Q	G
N	J	Y	M	C	X	R	G	G	T	Q	D	N	W	X
J	A	G	K	O	H	N	Y	T	I	C	H	I	M	U
N	A	M	E	I	G	O	O	B	C	O	H	I	E	J
A	X	X	F	X	U	E	B	M	S	Q	G	P	W	D
H	H	O	Y	H	E	M	J	O	Z	F	C	Y	F	S

BOOGIE MAN
GOBLIN
TREAT
WITCH

BROOMSTICK
JACK-O-LANTERN
TRICK

CANDY
PUMPKIN PATCH
VAMPIRE

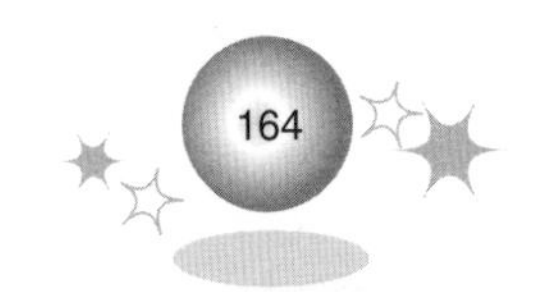

GREENHOUSE EFFECT!

Can you remember all that you see? Well, let's find out!
Study this picture carefully and then turn the page to answer some questions.
No peeking back at this page though!

QUESTIONS

1. What kind of flowers are in the first row of plants?
2. How many butterflies are around?
3. What is the gardener holding in his hands?
4. Is there fruit growing on the trees?
5. How many potted plants are there in the plant trolley?
6. Is someone using the watering can?
7. What temperature is set for the green house?
8. What tool is propped against the wall?
9. Who is sitting on the bench?
10. Is the hose attached to the tap?

WORD WOES!

Starting from the top, move down each step adding one letter as you go then rearrange all the letters around the 'T' to make a new word every time.

FRAMED!

Here's a mystery picture for you to identify. Just draw what you see in each of the numbered boxes into the blank boxes which have the same number on the opposite page.

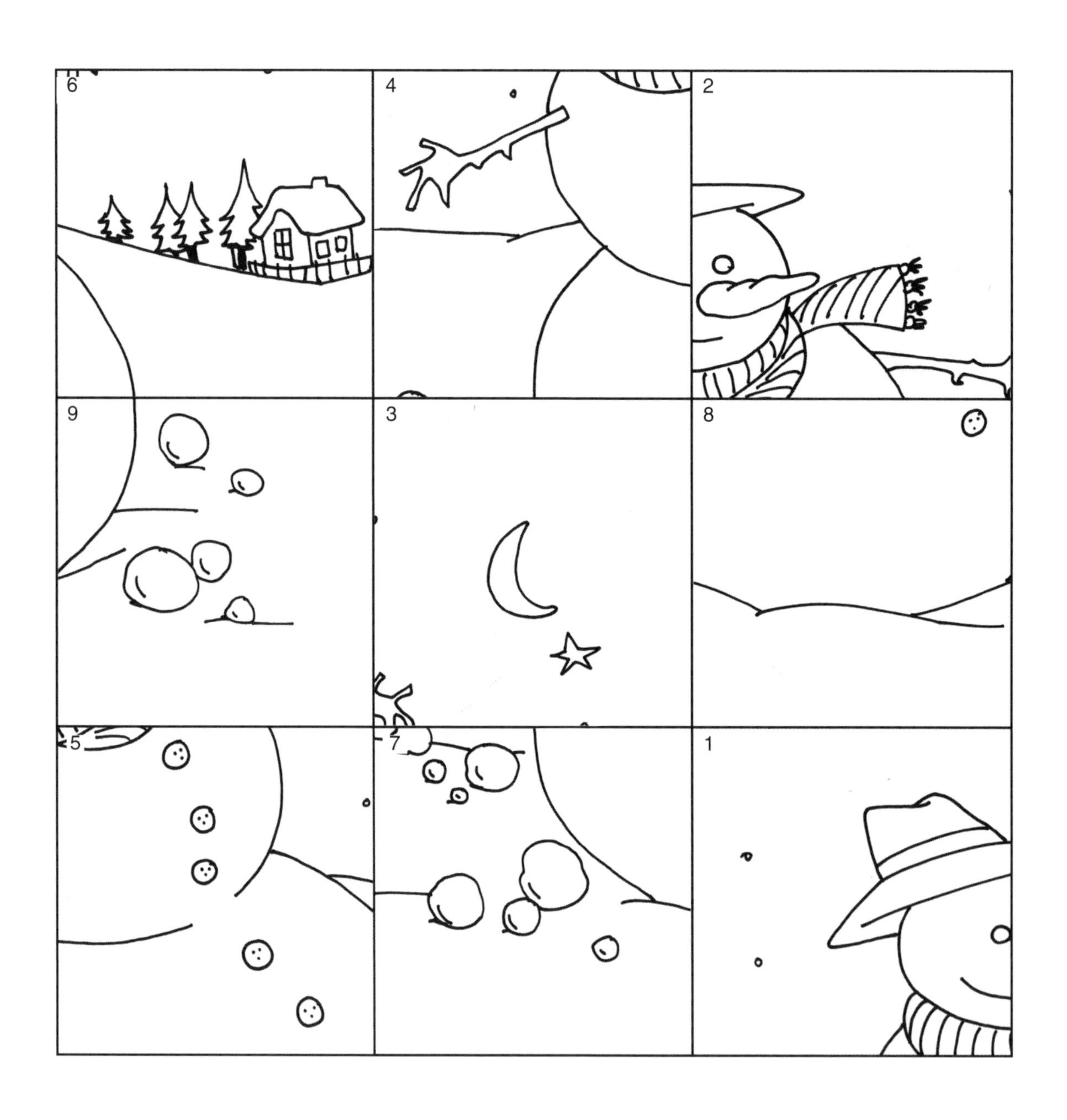

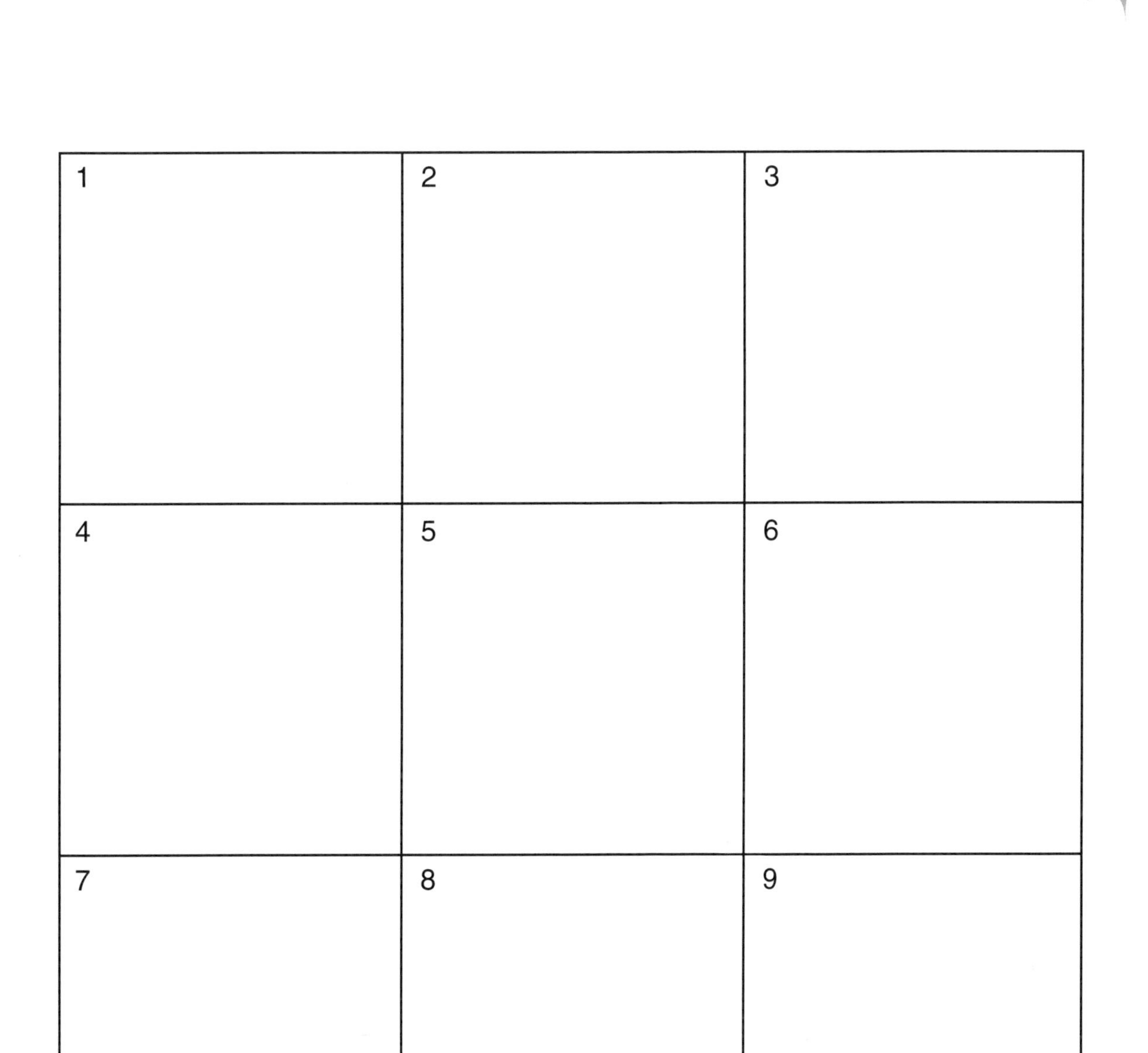
1
2
3
4
5
6
7
8
9

ORDER! ORDER!

These letters make a word when they are put in the right order. Track each letter along its path and then write it in its correct place to find out what the word is.

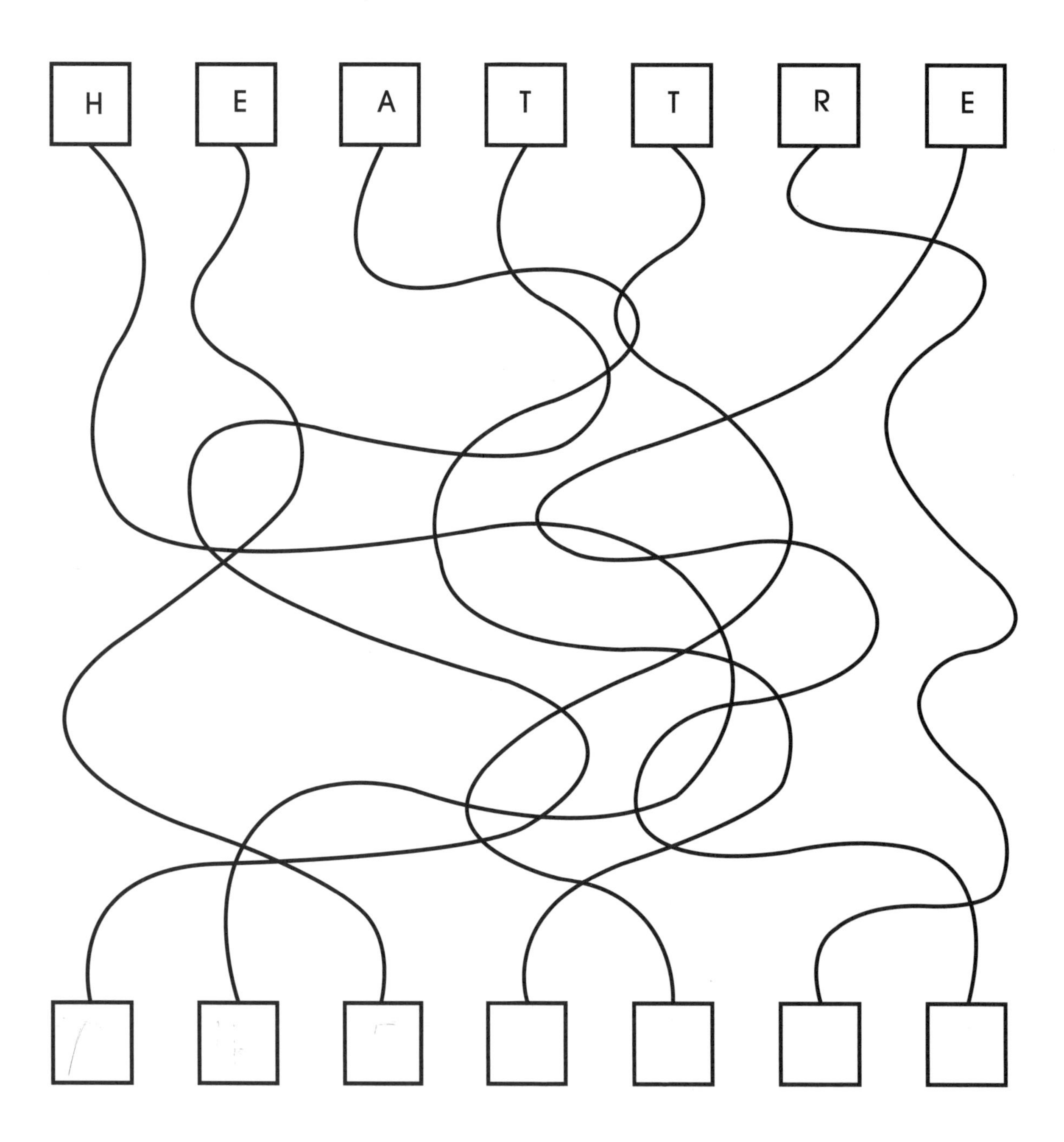

PYRAMID POINT!

Are the pyramids pointing up or are they pointing down?
Depends on how you look at them. Enjoy!

CROAK! CROAK!

The frog family is picnicking in the lily pond!
Look for all the objects listed below that are hidden in this picture.

Alien

Bowl of popcorn

Fork

Helicopter

Paper plane

Spider

Sun

Sunglasses

Umbrella

Walking stick

SOLVE IT!

How good are you at reading pictures? You had better be good!
Use the visual hints to correctly fill in the words in this picture crossword.

Across

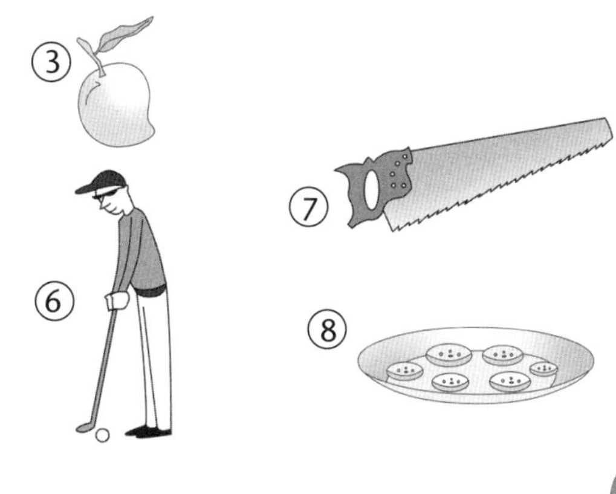

Down

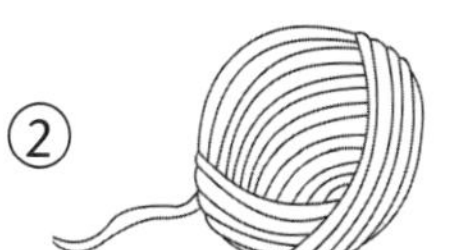

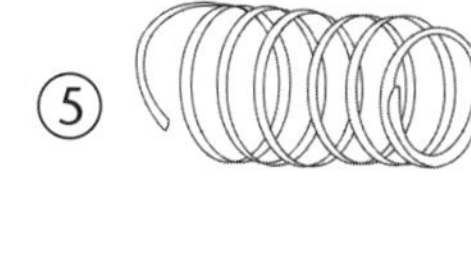

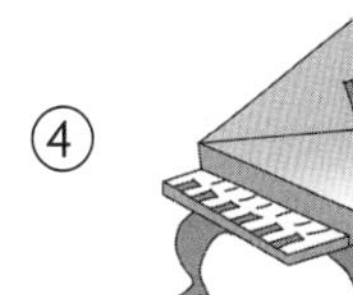

IT'S A RERUN!

There are two identical television sets in this group.
Look carefully and draw a circle around the two that are exactly the same.

WORD CENTRAL!

The first and last letters of some five letter words are given below.
How many can you think of?
To start you off, the first word could be SAUCE.

S _ _ _ E

S _ _ _ E

S _ _ _ E

S _ _ _ E

S _ _ _ E

S _ _ _ E

S _ _ _ E

S _ _ _ E

S _ _ _ E

S _ _ _ E

S _ _ _ E

S _ _ _ E

S _ _ _ E

S _ _ _ E

Good: 1 – 5

V. Good: 6 – 10

Excellent: 11 – 15

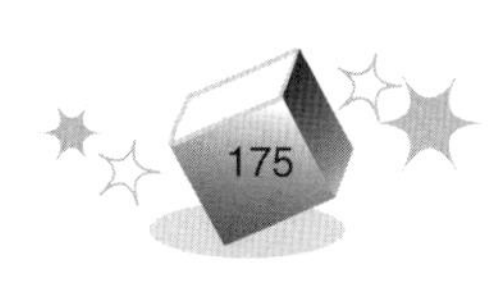

HOWZAT?

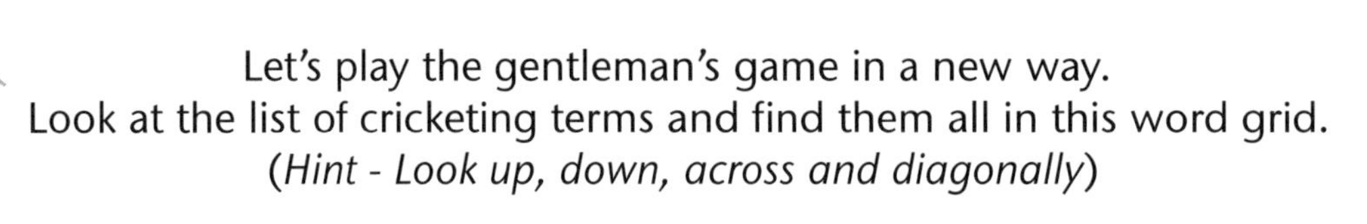

Let's play the gentleman's game in a new way.
Look at the list of cricketing terms and find them all in this word grid.
(*Hint - Look up, down, across and diagonally*)

B	U	E	Y	F	Z	P	Y	B	N	Q	M	G	E	N
B	O	U	N	D	A	R	Y	A	T	O	W	N	Q	K
H	W	W	N	T	T	C	Y	T	A	B	K	I	Z	I
E	I	N	L	R	G	Z	E	S	Z	E	T	D	Y	U
T	S	G	N	I	N	N	I	M	W	F	D	L	U	C
Y	E	L	C	U	N	S	R	A	O	I	G	E	C	E
K	G	K	I	H	P	G	G	N	H	O	Q	I	M	K
Q	T	K	C	P	Q	X	T	G	O	U	I	F	C	Z
H	W	A	U	I	U	A	C	G	D	B	J	I	H	I
K	N	M	G	R	W	E	B	A	C	O	R	E	P	Y
P	I	T	C	H	N	R	K	M	R	T	O	G	K	W
M	O	T	F	T	R	Q	T	S	T	S	F	F	X	L
Z	E	M	U	P	D	C	W	A	K	I	E	H	O	S
V	F	R	L	L	R	P	H	O	H	N	X	H	N	T
W	Y	U	Z	T	A	F	O	X	Z	C	V	R	K	E

BATSMAN	BOUNDARY	BOWLING
CENTURY	FIELDING	GOOGLY
HAT TRICK	HOWZAT	INNINGS
PITCH	SLIP	WICKET

GARAGE GALLERY!

Can you remember all that you see? Well, let's find out!
Study this picture carefully and then turn the page to answer some questions.
No peeking back at this page though!

QUESTIONS

1. Is the bonnet of the car open?
2. Is there a toolbox?
3. What is hanging on the back wall?
4. Are the batteries charged?
5. Is someone working underneath the car?
6. What is the little boy holding?
7. Has oil spilled on the floor?
8. Is there a tennis racket anywhere?
9. What does the number plate say?
10. Does the car have an aerial?

SPELLING BEE!

Starting from the top, move down each step adding one letter as you go then rearrange all the letters around the 'W' to make a new word every time.

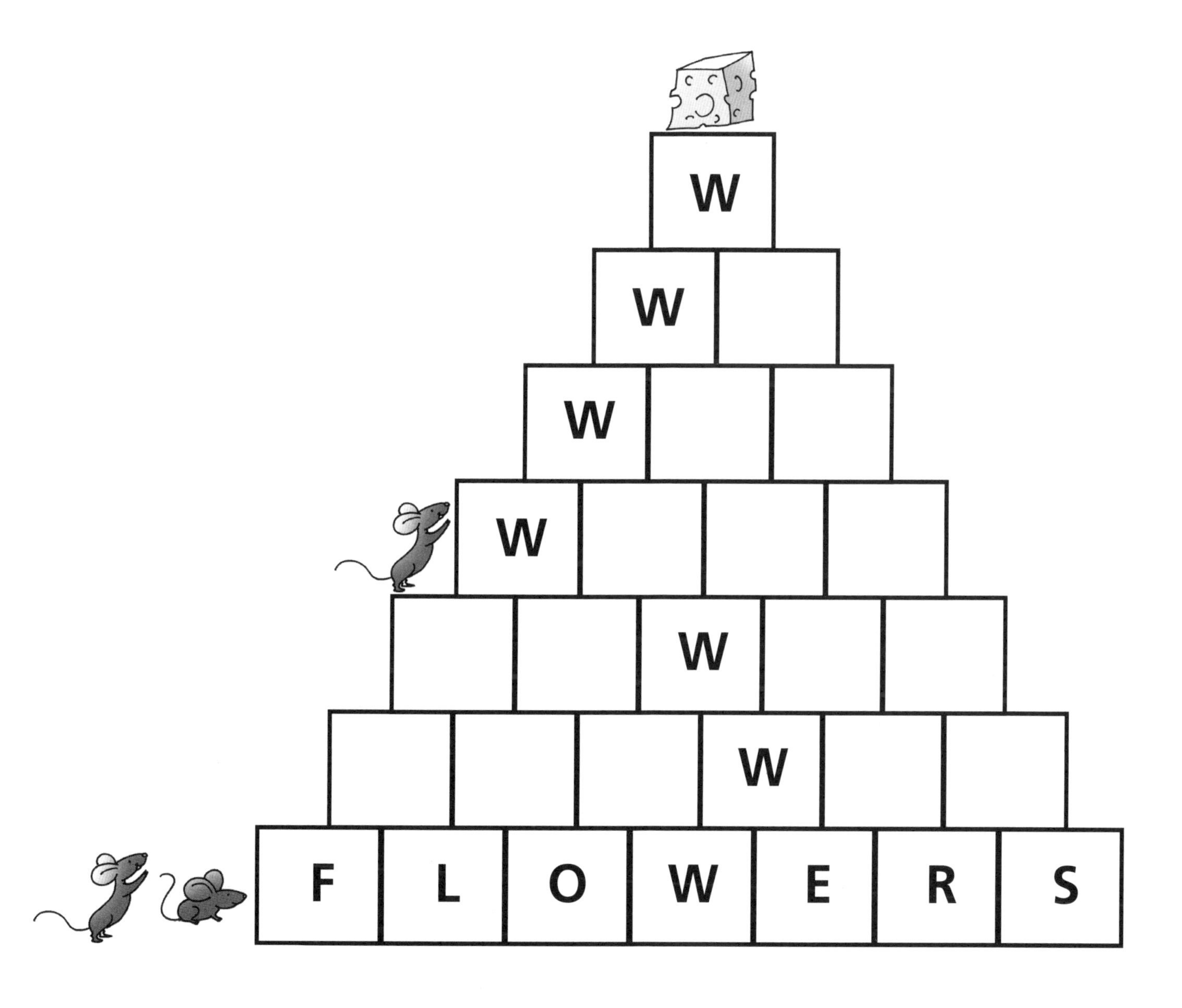

GRID GAMBOL!

Here's a mystery picture for you to identify.
Just draw what you see in each of the numbered boxes into
the blank boxes which have the same number on the opposite page.

1	2	3
4	5	6
7	8	9

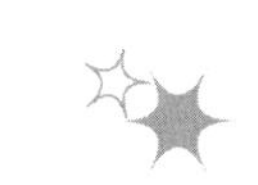

PLACEMENT!

These letters make a word when they are put in the right order.
Track each letter along its path and then write it in
its correct place to find out what the word is.

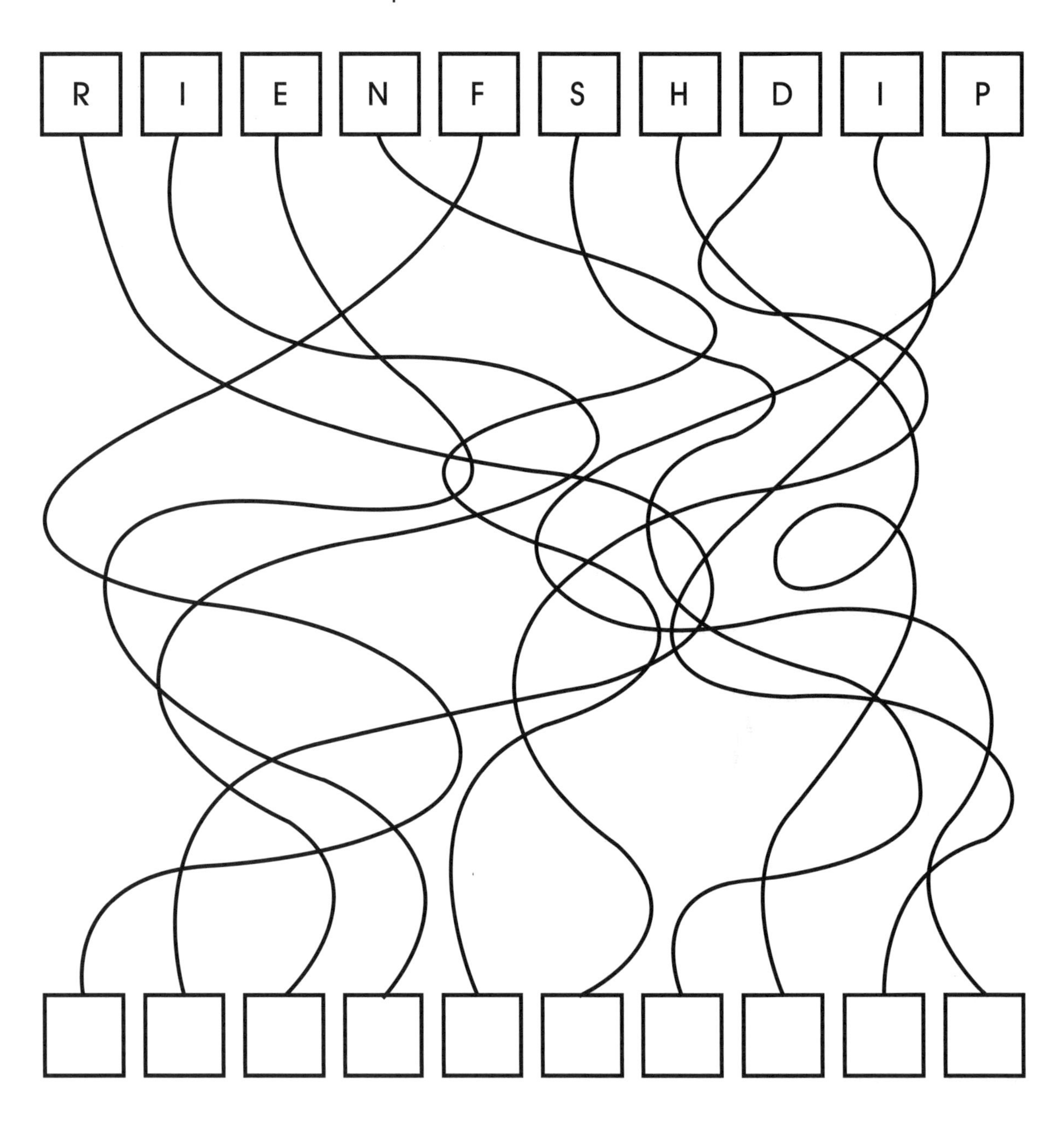

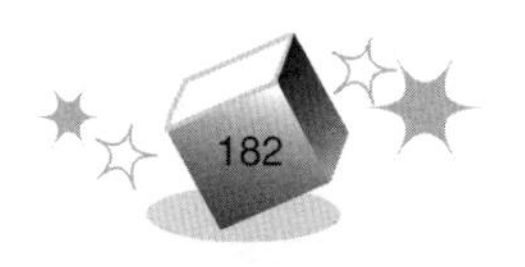

SIZE DOES MATTER!

Three soldiers in a row standing by a wall.
Can you work out which one is the tallest of them all?

ANSWERS

Page 4

Page 6

Page 7

1. FRUIT
2. FROST
3. FRONT
4. FLOAT
5. FLIRT
6. FLEET
7. FIRST
8. FIGHT
9. FEAST
10. FAULT
11. FAINT
12. FLINT

Page 5

Page 8

D	T	I	P	N	B	H	L	I	H	Y	J	D	G	H
I	S	H	K	I	N	L	U	E	J	C	D	C	A	W
A	N	P	U	P	U	R	U	Q	Z	D	H	N	Z	Z
M	O	P	T	M	I	A	N	I	B	N	S	V	C	R
R	W	C	P	N	B	K	V	W	Q	E	U	O	F	N
E	W	N	K	M	F	E	R	Y	L	B	C	P	B	A
M	H	T	D	R	J	E	L	A	A	X	F	A	A	P
E	I	D	O	O	H	G	N	I	D	I	R	D	E	R
L	T	L	S	Z	S	D	T	C	N	E	E	F	H	E
T	E	Z	P	R	G	U	X	Z	O	A	N	W	A	T
T	W	N	L	R	O	O	W	M	T	J	N	R	Z	E
I	M	W	E	S	T	V	F	O	T	L	Q	W	B	P
L	Y	T	C	I	N	D	E	R	E	L	L	A	V	E
Z	E	D	R	A	E	B	E	U	L	B	F	E	Z	I
L	E	K	Z	I	F	J	I	B	G	Y	V	E	F	C

Page 9-10

1. 4 o'clock
2. Four
3. No
4. On
5. A toy duck
6. A shawl
7. Yes
8. Yes
9. Spring
10. Yes

Page 11

Page 12-13

Page 14

Answer: AEROPLANE

Page 16

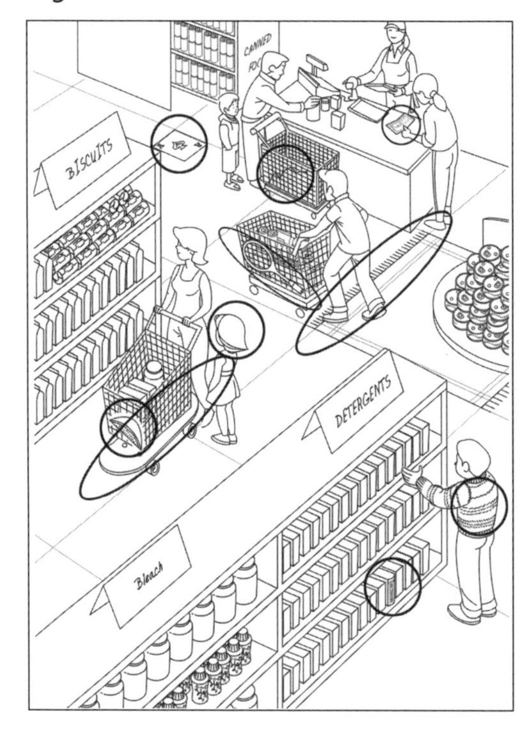

Page 17

		1 C	H	A	I	R
2 S		A				
3 K	I	N	G			
A		O				
T		4 E	G	G	5 S	
E					K	
		6 S			U	
7 M	I	T	T	E	N	S
		A			K	
		R				

Page 18

Page 19

1. HARSH
2. HITCH
3. HATCH
4. HUNCH
5. HEATH

Page 20

E	R	O	S	L	S	D	U	S	B	Q	R	B	G	Z
H	J	Z	I	W	O	L	X	Z	K	L	Y	P	O	M
W	B	O	O	M	R	H	Y	V	W	L	S	E	T	H
B	N	O	R	A	E	B	X	P	D	S	M	N	B	H
R	L	A	E	X	C	I	P	B	W	D	A	P	X	V
V	Z	G	P	O	O	F	D	I	X	H	W	Z	X	G
O	O	Y	L	P	N	H	W	K	P	Q	O	K	B	S
D	R	K	N	C	I	G	A	E	I	F	C	T	I	C
V	B	E	D	Z	H	N	L	E	O	P	E	V	V	K
H	H	I	E	H	R	E	H	Y	U	T	Z	K	N	O
O	B	E	N	D	Z	V	T	H	J	W	I	M	Q	Z
R	K	U	A	V	Y	H	Q	C	D	Z	D	G	G	Z
S	X	D	C	E	C	N	M	U	K	J	R	C	E	B
E	Y	P	T	C	W	M	O	N	K	E	Y	V	F	R
H	S	G	J	D	U	N	H	G	B	G	Q	W	N	B

Page 21-22

1. Yes
2. Two
3. Long strap
4. No
5. Things to do
6. 10 pounds
7. Oval
8. No
9. Fresh Mint
10. No

Page 23

Page 24-25

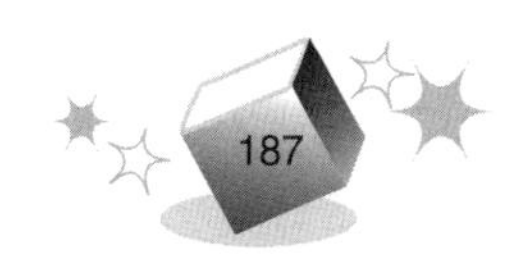

Page 26

Answer: CIRCUS

Page 28

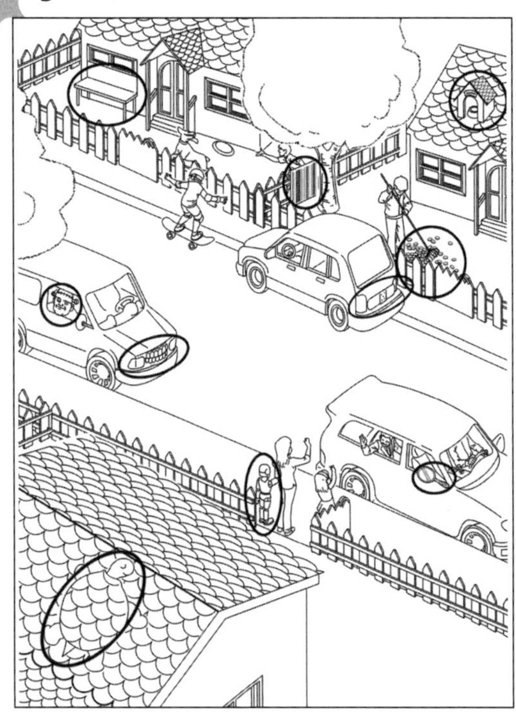

Page 29

Page 30

Page 31

1. GRAPE
2. GOOSE
3. GRADE
4. GRATE
5. GLARE
6. GLAZE
7. GLIDE
8. GLOBE
9. GLOVE
10. GRACE
11. GRAZE
12. GUIDE

Page 32

R	B	R	W	E	L	L	S	Z	F	Y	I	Z	P	F
L	E	D	E	T	D	V	R	O	I	B	J	L	C	S
Q	J	L	P	D	Q	U	D	L	F	T	Y	V	P	C
R	M	R	D	H	D	D	B	S	T	S	P	A	G	D
V	B	I	F	D	E	E	G	W	G	W	P	X	W	E
T	P	D	U	R	O	E	N	S	E	M	D	Z	S	Z
L	U	D	I	K	L	T	R	Y	V	G	A	E	X	K
Q	S	L	F	D	E	L	D	D	A	T	T	Y	X	Y
P	H	E	D	Q	V	I	J	Q	G	T	G	S	W	N
H	C	U	U	Y	S	V	N	Z	E	C	M	J	I	O
U	F	W	A	D	D	L	E	V	L	B	J	W	M	A
Z	K	V	F	C	L	T	N	B	D	A	X	O	M	I
O	E	E	A	O	K	G	U	O	D	T	N	F	P	P
E	L	D	D	A	R	T	S	E	I	X	X	X	Q	P
W	F	R	A	F	S	W	N	Q	M	W	F	F	O	B

Page 33-34

1. History
2. Two
3. 25.9.06
4. No
5. One
6. Striped
7. Yes
8. Two
9. Yes
10. Yes

Page 35

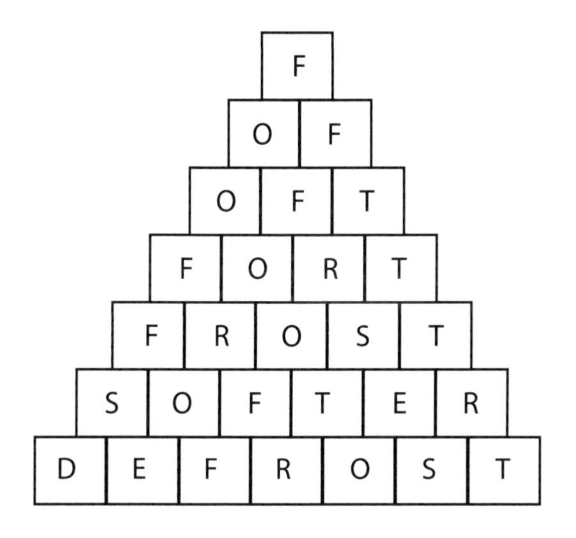

Page 36-37

Page 38

Answer: SCHOOLBUS

Page 40

Page 41

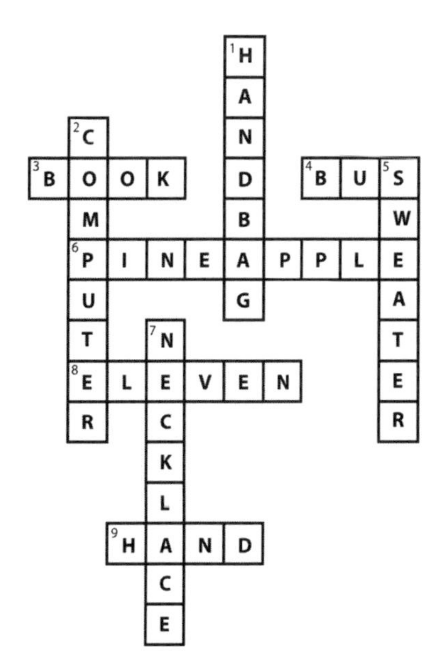

Page 42

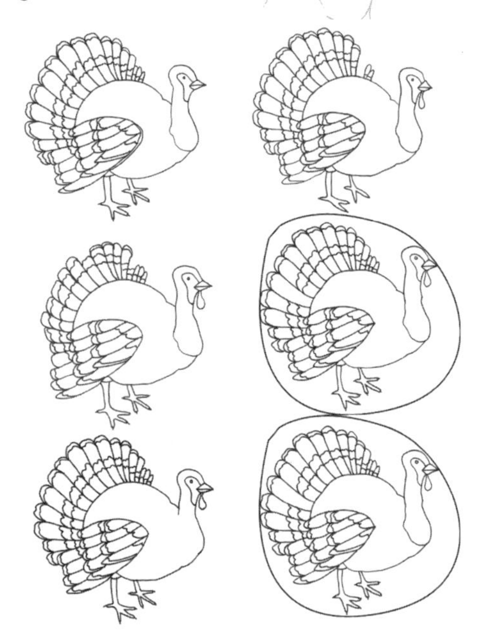

Page 43

1. OCCUR
2. ODOUR
3. OFFER
4. OLDER
5. ORDER
6. OTHER
7. OUTER
8. OWNER
9. OTTER
10. OILER

Page 44

M	N	F	E	B	F	Q	N	I	E	Y	K	T	J	W
T	O	O	Q	A	E	L	G	R	R	Z	N	C	T	Z
F	H	D	U	F	R	L	O	R	P	K	A	O	Y	D
R	H	J	G	G	P	P	G	A	C	N	I	M	M	N
J	C	I	B	N	A	O	F	I	I	S	L	C	A	R
I	Y	Z	E	G	I	R	N	Y	U	K	A	A	W	L
L	D	H	N	U	A	K	B	Z	D	M	R	N	G	Y
O	U	I	K	N	D	I	D	T	W	I	T	A	D	S
R	S	N	C	D	N	I	U	E	A	B	S	D	J	C
Y	S	E	C	X	S	A	C	L	T	U	U	A	Y	S
R	P	F	L	N	A	W	I	A	T	I	A	O	L	I
V	B	M	L	V	B	P	B	D	O	N	N	M	A	T
G	E	R	M	A	N	Y	K	I	N	I	V	U	T	Y
V	W	H	I	O	G	M	Y	M	P	I	R	H	I	C
Y	Z	C	G	U	V	V	U	J	Z	D	S	K	R	W

Page 45-46

1. No
2. Yes
3. Yes
4. Yes
5. 4 o'clock
6. No
7. Three
8. No
9. No
10. Air way

Page 47

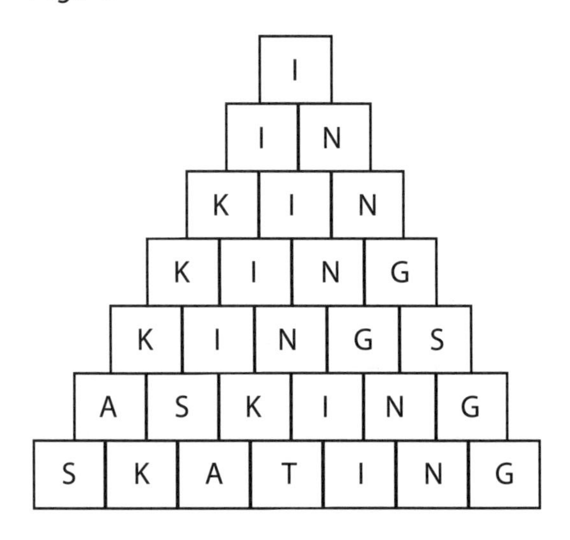

Page 48-49

Page 50

Answer: CHRISTMAS

Page 52

Page 53

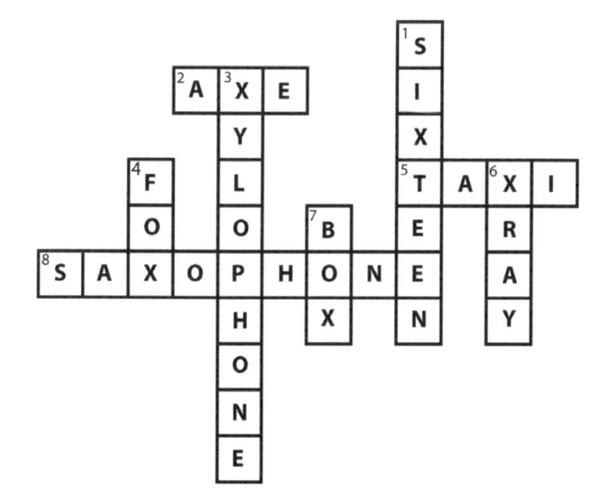

Page 54

Page 55

1. PASTE
2. PAUSE
3. PEACE
4. PEEVE
5. PENCE
6. PHONE
7. PIECE
8. PLACE
9. PLANE
10. PLATE
11. PRICE
12. PRIME
13. PRIDE
14. PRIZE
15. PURSE

Page 56

R	N	E	X	K	R	N	L	M	V	A	A	L	G	J
L	E	A	K	V	X	O	E	P	R	P	A	N	X	S
J	P	H	D	F	B	S	C	A	E	M	O	H	H	T
B	V	P	C	R	Q	Y	L	L	R	R	M	F	K	E
T	L	Y	Q	A	O	T	F	X	T	F	E	Y	R	F
B	X	Q	B	H	M	J	P	S	Q	X	N	A	A	F
J	Y	B	S	M	E	U	M	S	A	I	T	A	K	I
V	G	F	A	D	D	R	H	H	W	R	G	Q	L	T
B	E	C	K	H	A	M	O	C	V	A	W	Y	U	N
A	N	E	R	E	S	S	K	N	S	R	Z	G	D	A
F	P	C	L	D	E	N	D	S	A	J	Y	D	N	Q
F	Q	O	G	U	W	G	I	B	A	L	N	J	E	V
N	S	A	Q	F	L	K	L	M	T	T	D	K	T	A
B	E	P	K	I	L	T	G	C	H	V	L	O	J	E
K	C	J	O	H	T	Z	F	D	A	B	W	V	E	D

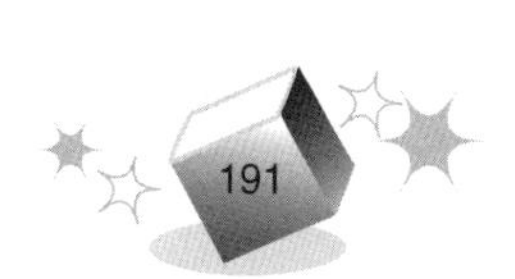

Page 57-58

1. Yes
2. Sitting
3. Pears
4. Geese
5. A rabbit
6. Cowboy hat
7. Grow Well
8. Three
9. Climbing the tree
10. Hanging from the scarecrow's hand

Page 59

Page 60-61

Page 62

Answer: HISTORY

Page 64

Page 65

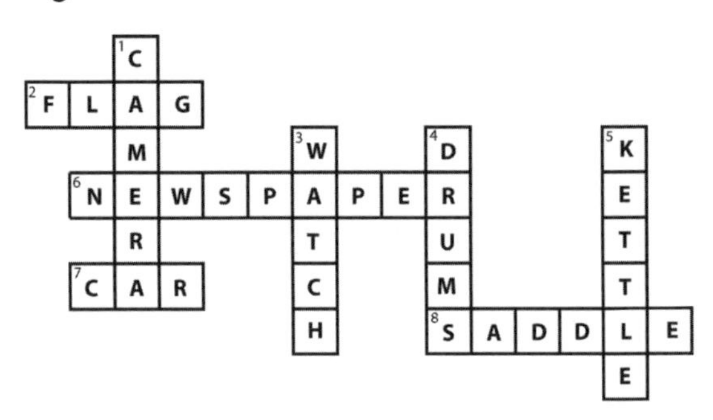

Page 66

Page 67

1. ACTOR
2. ADDER
3. AFTER
4. ALDER
5. ALTAR
6. ALTER
7. AMBER
8. ANGER
9. ASTER
10. ABHOR

Page 68

P	X	D	Y	Y	U	W	K	Y	B	A	M	G	F	T
Q	O	U	K	W	Q	I	A	A	I	S	B	I	L	U
W	X	P	Q	H	F	L	K	W	O	E	T	R	U	N
O	F	T	L	G	Q	L	B	H	E	P	T	G	E	T
Y	B	O	X	A	G	O	Y	C	U	S	I	G	H	S
N	X	B	R	T	R	W	H	C	V	H	D	S	J	E
G	S	D	Y	C	W	A	L	N	U	T	A	X	T	H
P	L	U	J	H	I	K	A	E	T	V	Q	Q	D	C
X	Y	F	X	L	C	Q	F	W	X	S	F	W	E	L
N	L	W	G	S	J	B	B	L	S	A	X	M	Q	G
E	E	D	Z	G	E	U	K	E	E	J	R	V	B	K
O	K	U	U	T	V	V	R	F	D	B	K	B	M	H
T	W	G	F	Q	J	P	K	Y	F	U	C	N	L	S
S	K	M	G	W	Y	E	J	L	K	N	T	J	E	T
E	Z	F	Z	C	S	Z	M	J	D	K	T	L	O	E

Page 69-70

1. No
2. The best cook
3. Yes
4. Four
5. Yes
6. Carrots
7. Yes
8. Three
9. Yes
10. No, there are coffee mugs

Page 71

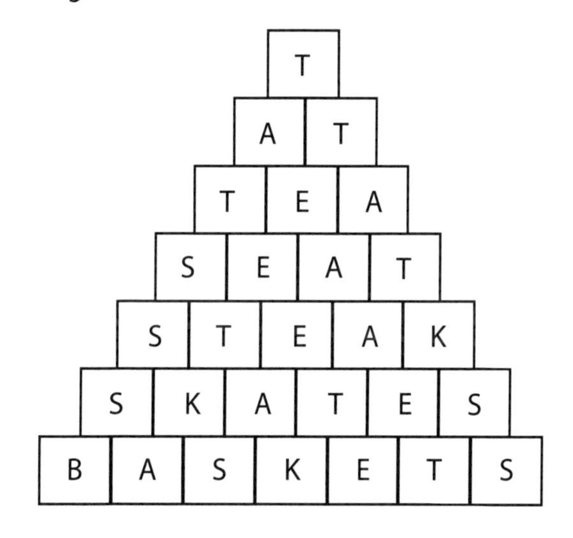

Page 72-73

Page 74

Answer: MONSOON

Page 76

Page 77

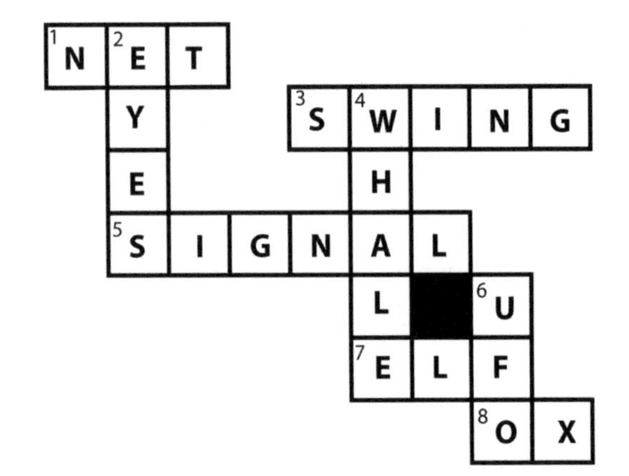

Page 78

Page 79

1. VALUE
2. VAGUE
3. VOICE
4. VERSE
5. VALVE
6. VENUE
7. VERGE

Page 80

H	A	A	C	K	E	W	E	U	D	Y	I	I	T	O
L	S	J	T	M	Z	H	D	Q	L	N	J	P	U	Y
B	W	I	Z	N	W	A	Y	Y	O	Q	J	I	C	I
W	K	N	F	T	L	L	J	A	M	W	Y	R	J	W
G	A	V	F	D	R	E	D	P	R	P	A	N	U	T
V	U	N	L	J	L	O	X	F	R	E	I	Q	P	H
V	C	O	S	B	F	O	U	Z	C	V	D	N	X	Q
Q	W	M	W	K	D	E	G	T	W	H	O	Q	G	L
U	K	I	G	N	D	N	T	L	X	M	G	V	J	D
D	U	N	B	M	P	I	B	F	L	S	H	A	R	K
L	D	A	N	W	O	D	W	A	K	E	V	M	E	D
K	S	P	R	M	F	R	S	C	R	F	E	C	M	Q
S	L	U	A	K	D	A	V	X	A	Y	V	Y	G	K
A	V	I	D	K	F	S	U	J	A	Q	C	Y	G	H
C	E	X	N	D	I	Z	U	X	E	B	B	D	U	S

Page 81-82

1. A parrot
2. On the sofa
3. Bruno
4. Three
5. No
6. Snoozing
7. A squirrel
8. Yes
9. No
10. Yes

Page 83

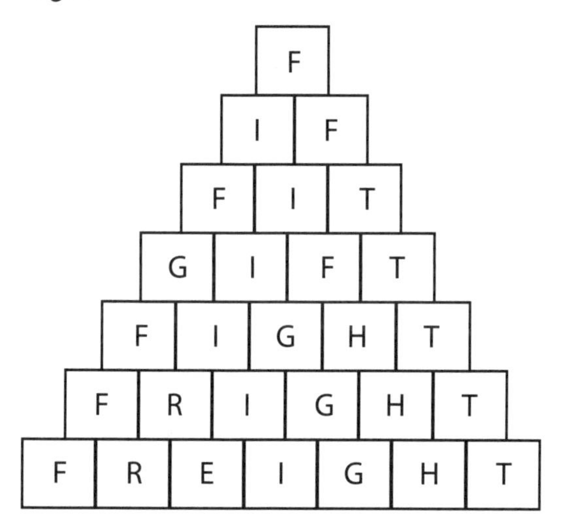

Page 84-85

Page 86

Answer: COMPUTER

Page 88

Page 89

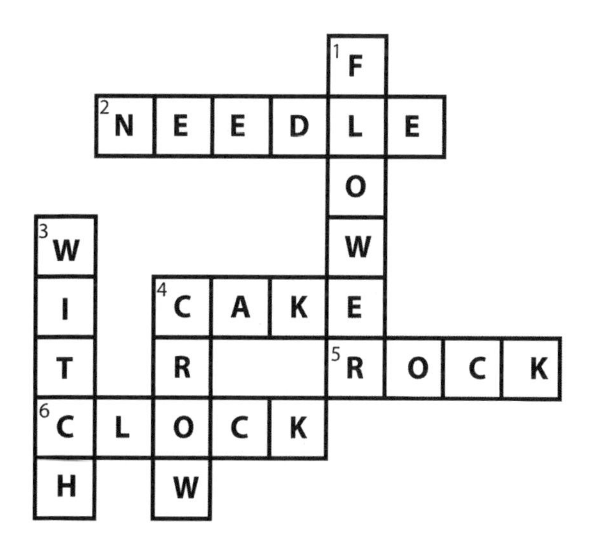

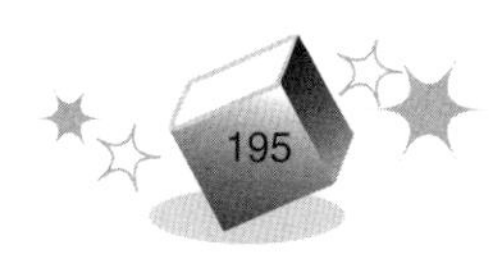

Page 90

Page 91

1. BOOST
2. BOAST
3. BLEAT
4. BLURT
5. BLUNT
6. BLEST
7. BLEAT
8. BERET
9. BEAST
10. BURST
11. BUILT
12. BURNT

Page 92

E	Y	K	S	G	W	K	J	K	H	I	R	J	H	S
D	L	S	E	V	N	B	N	O	D	O	E	P	Y	P
D	Q	T	T	R	A	A	M	Q	M	B	T	N	N	I
L	R	I	T	C	H	E	F	E	B	W	T	X	M	D
U	H	D	D	I	A	S	N	P	O	V	O	G	I	E
T	E	M	O	L	L	G	Z	V	C	U	P	G	W	R
P	L	G	O	L	N	T	I	E	F	S	Y	U	N	M
G	H	N	C	I	I	P	R	F	D	S	R	Q	Q	A
Q	E	E	D	S	P	T	Q	A	S	J	R	O	S	N
P	U	N	R	S	Z	R	T	X	U	O	A	W	Y	Y
N	I	L	H	V	F	K	G	L	I	T	H	N	E	J
F	S	H	A	R	K	T	A	L	E	S	S	G	E	E
G	N	I	K	N	O	I	L	P	A	Z	Z	A	O	A
Z	W	P	I	X	R	W	T	D	S	W	X	Q	R	R
N	W	T	D	E	D	T	G	X	Y	L	U	L	A	N

Page 93-94

1. A clown
2. Unicycle
3. Yes
4. None
5. Yes
6. Santa Claus
7. Have a nice day
8. He wants to shoot hoops
9. Yes
10. One pound

Page 95

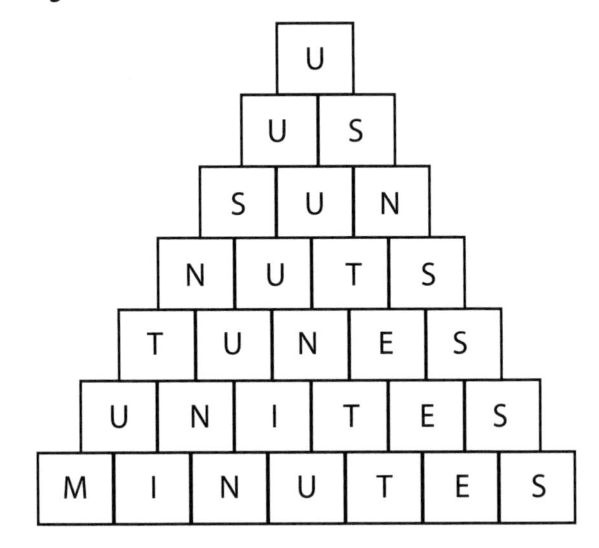

Page 96-97

Page 98

Answer: HALLOWEEN

Page 100

Page 101

Page 102

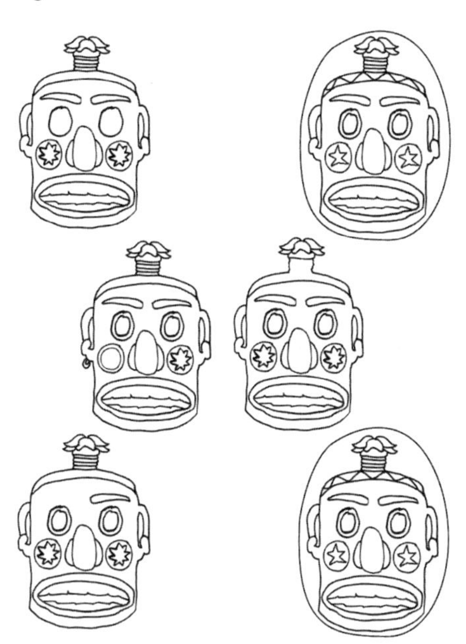

Page 103

1. CYCLE
2. CURVE
3. CLONE
4. CRAZE
5. CRATE
6. CLOSE
7. CURSE
8. CHORE
9. CHASE
10. CAUSE
11. CASTE
12. CEASE
13. CANOE
14. CABLE
15. CARVE

Page 104

B	Q	E	H	R	J	Y	U	H	Q	E	C	M	H	N
D	S	M	L	X	W	N	J	L	H	O	R	A	R	G
W	G	R	J	C	N	A	O	E	M	W	I	N	E	Q
X	C	P	C	H	Y	L	T	P	K	J	K	C	T	N
V	R	N	H	A	L	C	U	C	P	P	I	C	A	J
L	N	L	O	U	E	T	I	Q	H	M	P	C	E	Z
L	A	G	C	S	E	V	I	B	C	W	R	F	W	K
J	G	S	O	R	S	R	E	N	I	A	R	T	S	N
L	U	W	L	V	J	Q	O	J	H	O	I	E	X	G
E	X	A	A	B	O	O	K	S	V	C	H	L	P	N
T	N	Q	T	W	T	A	B	H	T	T	N	J	Y	X
F	G	B	E	T	M	C	L	X	O	G	J	M	Q	V
O	A	Q	S	D	A	X	U	L	Y	O	J	N	C	G
U	A	R	W	F	E	F	C	H	S	T	D	S	U	O
A	G	E	X	U	B	P	E	O	E	F	S	A	V	J

Page 105-106

1. No
2. Fine weather
3. A straw hat
4. Yes
5. Yes
6. On the horizon
7. A pelican
8. Scuba diving
9. Captain Hook
10. Two

Page 107

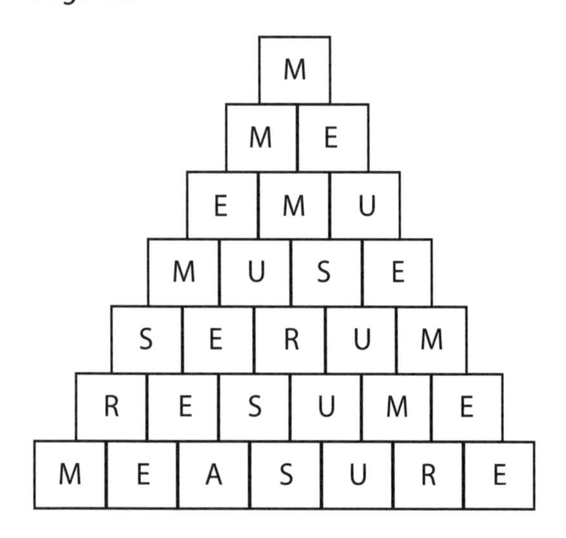

Page 108-109

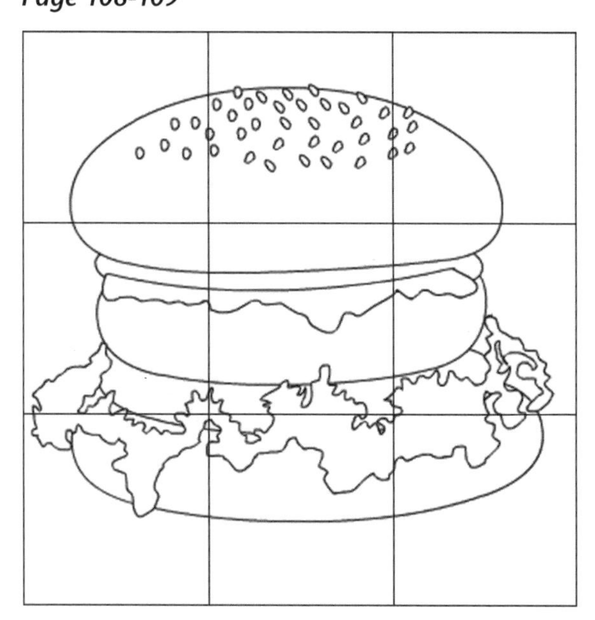

Page 110

Answer: MIDDAY

Page 112

Page 113

			1 M	A	2 S	K		3 C
					U			A
	4 B	5 A	G	P	I	P	E	S
		S			T			T
		T						L
		R						E
	6 M	O	N	K	E	Y		
		N						
7 L	E	A	F					
		U						
		T						

Page 114

Page 115

1. MOVIE
2. MOUSE
3. MOOSE
4. MINCE
5. METRE
6. MERGE
7. MIDGE
8. MAYBE
9. MAPLE
10. MAIZE
11. MELEE
12. MAUVE

Page 116

E	S	T	G	E	L	Y	C	N	W	L	U	M	D	M
I	J	U	G	K	T	S	G	M	P	G	U	C	A	A
C	S	A	N	P	L	O	L	O	Y	M	T	C	F	I
P	E	S	V	F	R	G	V	A	E	N	I	R	F	D
M	S	B	V	C	L	F	M	H	Z	K	K	X	O	S
O	V	I	H	V	Q	O	T	P	G	U	W	Y	D	J
W	L	I	Z	F	X	N	W	X	Y	M	Z	D	I	C
X	D	I	E	O	A	T	C	E	I	Z	O	V	L	B
E	W	S	K	S	Y	B	T	J	R	N	C	S	R	P
R	O	R	Y	G	G	X	E	E	O	Y	G	W	E	K
R	E	R	T	E	L	O	I	V	U	J	S	A	T	K
B	H	A	P	E	L	A	P	S	Q	E	C	I	S	D
C	Q	O	B	C	A	R	N	A	T	I	O	N	A	K
L	I	L	Y	Y	U	G	L	V	Z	C	W	D	X	D
E	H	Y	E	K	S	Y	Z	E	I	P	R	Z	F	C

Page 117-118

1. Yes
2. Yes
3. Yes
4. Biscuits
5. Two
6. No
7. Two
8. From a test tube
9. Yes
10. Chemistry class

Page 119

Page 120-121

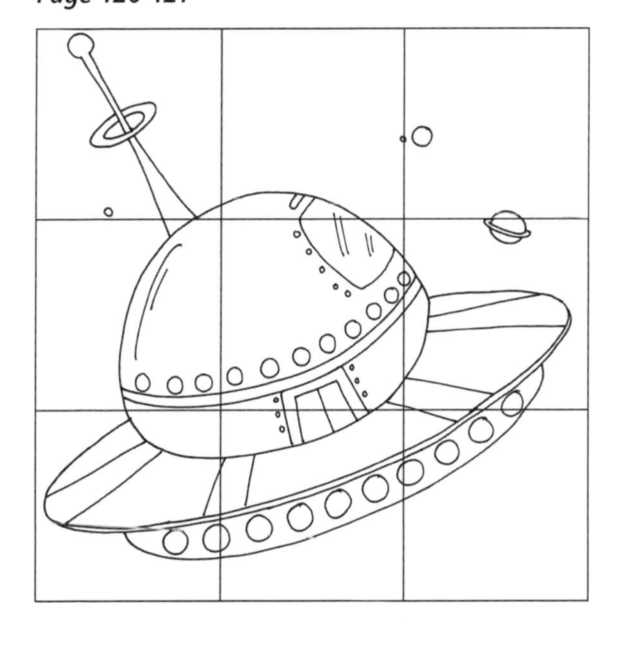

Page 122

Answer: FOUNTAIN

Page 124

Page 125

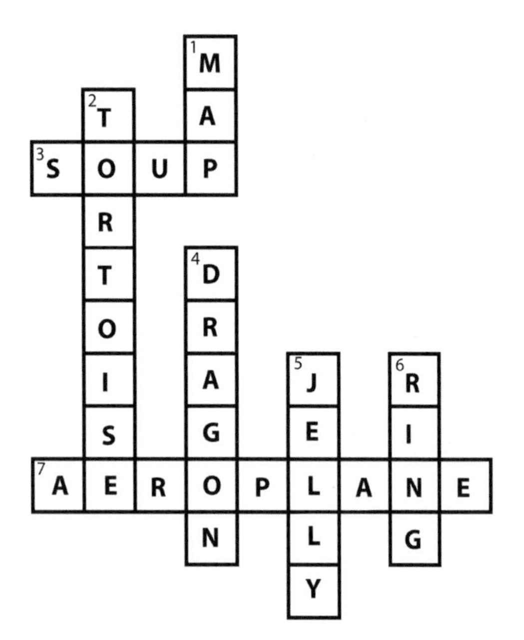

Page 126

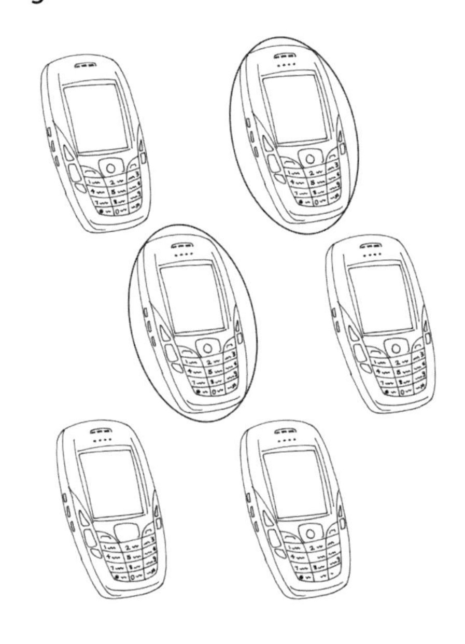

Page 127

1. ROOST
2. ROBOT
3. ROAST
4. RIGHT
5. REACT

Page 128

N	D	D	H	E	H	U	C	M	L	N	R	Z	N	J
O	Q	W	T	T	Q	Z	B	X	E	M	Y	I	V	O
S	N	Z	S	O	E	U	M	D	S	C	W	V	G	H
L	Q	P	N	U	N	T	E	J	A	D	E	G	E	N
I	B	Z	Z	U	H	Y	H	H	L	G	S	W	N	M
W	E	O	S	B	N	J	B	A	L	W	M	U	P	A
D	K	B	Q	O	N	R	B	L	J	R	T	W	K	J
L	D	Z	H	R	N	Y	G	K	A	L	I	Q	F	O
O	K	T	T	Q	E	L	C	S	Y	I	E	F	R	R
R	N	L	S	L	P	Q	L	H	N	J	R	A	R	F
A	U	Q	N	E	D	W	A	R	D	H	E	A	T	H
H	J	A	N	D	R	E	W	L	A	W	N	R	L	D
P	T	O	T	B	T	E	Y	M	N	R	D	A	V	E
S	N	A	H	G	A	L	L	A	C	S	E	M	A	J
O	E	E	A	T	W	Y	W	H	K	Z	W	E	E	M

Page 129-130

1. Turkey
2. Six
3. Yes
4. Yes
5. Flowers
6. Yes
7. Yes
8. Yes
9. No
10. Strawberry ice-cream

Page 131

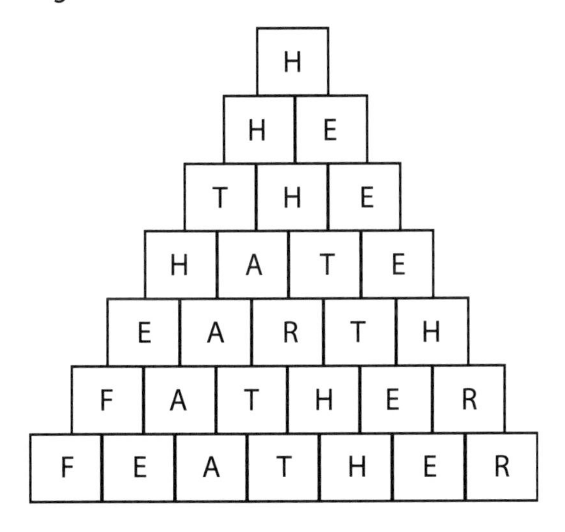

Page 132-133

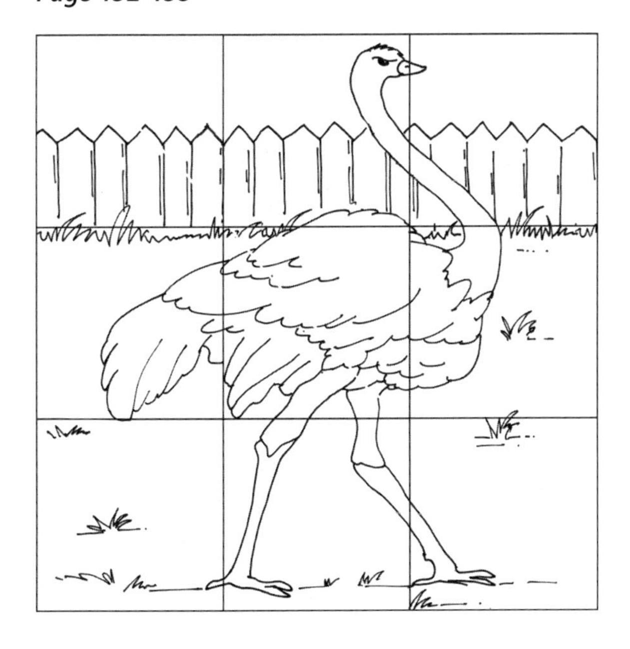

Page 134

Answer: LIBRARIAN

Page 136

Page 137

		[1] S		[2] T					
		T		E					
[3] H		A		L			[4] B	E	D
O		R		E			O		
R		F		S			N		
[5] S	U	I	T	C	A	S	E		
E		S		O					
		H		P					
				E					

Page 138

Page 139

1. LASER
2. LATER
3. LEVER
4. LAYER
5. LIVER
6. LOSER
7. LOWER
8. LUNAR
9. LINER
10. LAGER

Page 140

W	E	X	H	Z	G	N	E	B	T	U	P	O	Q	Q
P	I	N	E	A	P	P	L	E	A	S	A	F	G	V
N	E	G	N	A	R	O	P	W	Q	N	P	R	T	N
O	E	L	Y	I	I	J	P	T	A	B	A	X	G	O
L	S	P	P	M	B	U	A	S	H	P	Y	N	K	Y
E	F	M	J	P	S	C	D	I	E	L	A	S	A	Y
M	L	H	S	X	A	I	R	S	V	W	C	X	R	O
V	U	X	F	X	U	T	A	A	N	H	O	R	G	S
L	V	L	B	T	F	O	T	E	H	A	E	N	B	A
P	S	I	H	Z	K	Z	S	N	A	B	A	M	O	R
C	V	F	W	H	C	U	U	D	W	M	S	I	A	X
O	T	A	D	B	V	G	C	A	H	F	Q	H	F	Y
L	E	D	O	L	Z	N	R	G	Z	N	K	E	V	M
N	L	R	K	L	N	T	B	P	D	Z	K	O	M	I
I	F	M	A	I	S	Y	F	D	L	M	J	T	L	F

Page 141-142

1. Two
2. Father
3. Dinosaurs
4. One
5. An Owl
6. No
7. Mother
8. Yes
9. Nine
10. On the shelf

Page 143

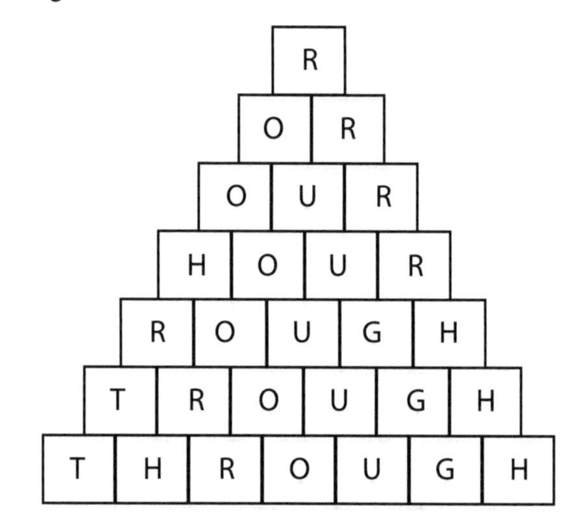

Page 144-145

Page 146

Answer: MARTIAN

Page 148

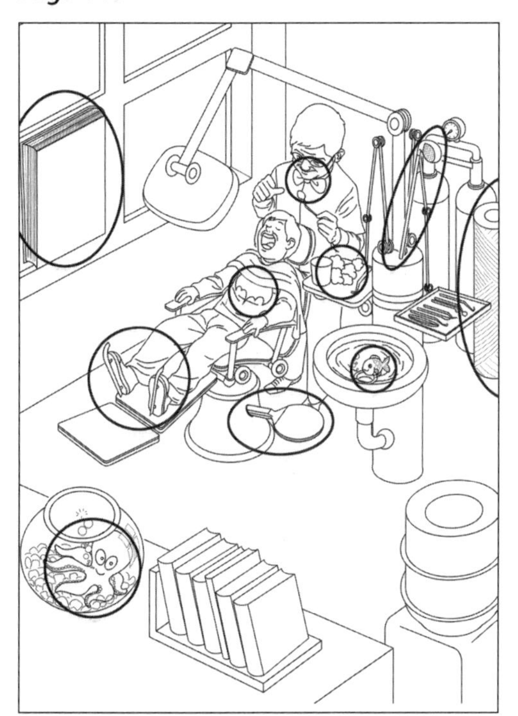

Page 149

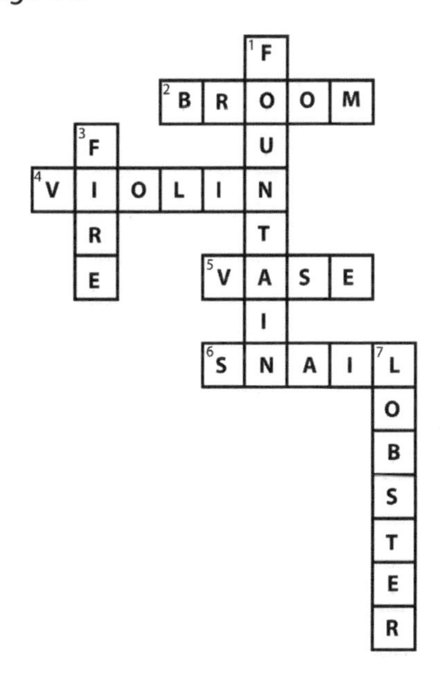

Page 150

Page 151

1. NIECE
2. NOISE
3. NURSE
4. NERVE
5. NOBLE

Page 152

S	Y	B	X	U	C	X	A	A	N	A	L	J	B	V
X	I	Y	A	V	I	P	Z	O	V	C	L	C	C	X
C	W	N	V	S	T	U	T	H	Y	W	A	E	Y	Q
B	X	Y	N	E	E	N	H	F	I	Y	B	N	L	O
C	Z	B	N	E	I	B	O	A	B	B	T	C	A	D
J	P	N	B	M	T	L	A	O	S	G	E	R	V	U
F	I	I	D	O	O	E	H	L	F	U	K	I	G	P
S	C	A	S	P	P	J	L	S	L	R	S	C	O	J
Y	B	G	N	I	X	O	B	B	A	K	A	K	D	T
F	O	O	T	B	A	L	L	V	A	U	B	E	F	Z
R	R	X	E	L	U	S	S	E	V	T	Q	T	H	F
K	C	N	L	E	V	Q	I	W	S	K	G	S	W	S
P	I	B	G	V	E	T	L	Q	A	W	R	O	P	F
M	V	Y	F	Q	Z	U	V	K	B	U	Q	E	R	L
E	F	T	V	R	Y	Z	B	Z	Z	G	N	O	Z	L

Page 153-154

1. Circular
2. Yes
3. White Wash
4. No
5. A cat
6. Two
7. Yes
8. Yes
9. Talking on the phone
10. Yes

Page 155

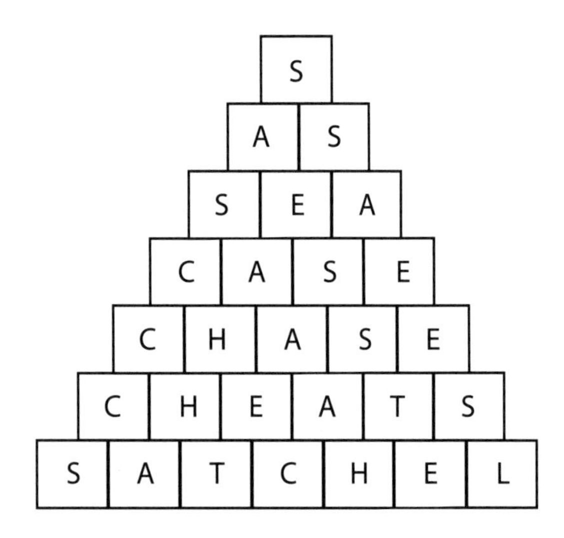

Page 156-157

Page 158

Answer: SATURN

Page 160

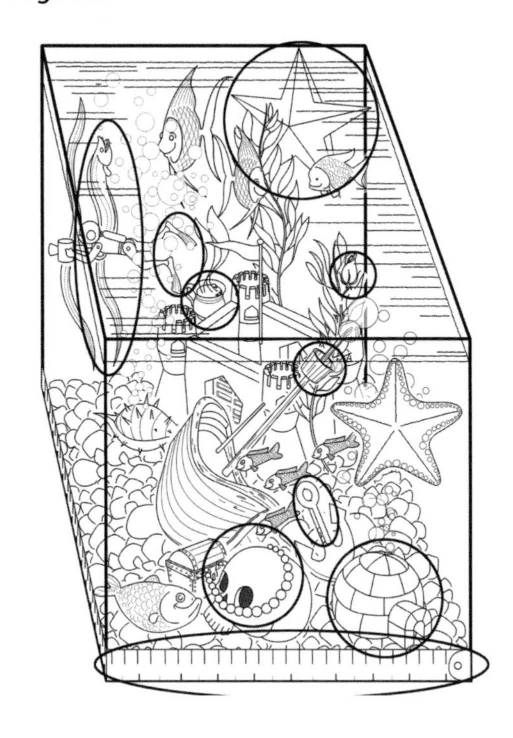

Page 161

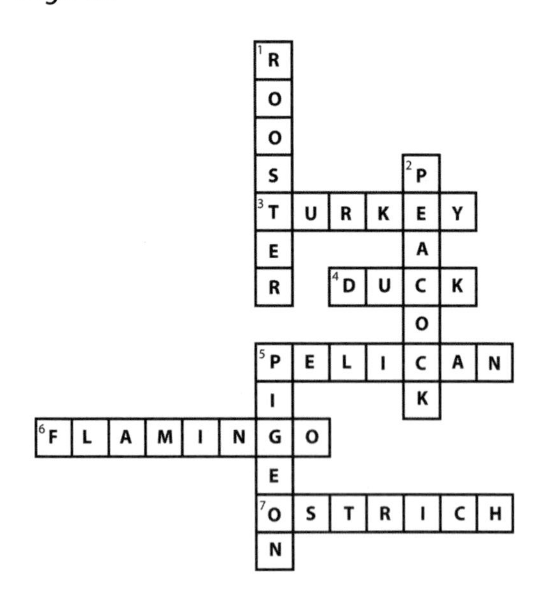

Page 162

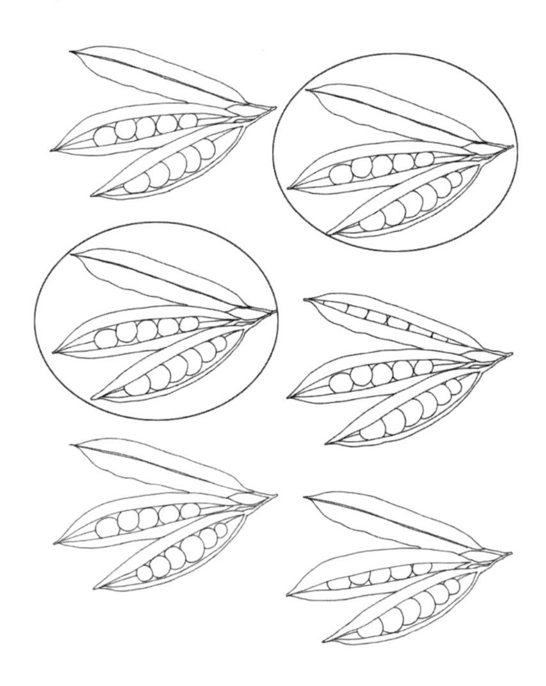

Page 163

1. WATCH
2. WEIGH
3. WHICH
4. WIDTH
5. WITCH
6. WORTH
7. WRATH

Page 164

T	R	E	A	T	C	J	E	B	W	U	X	K	J	U
P	P	O	O	D	A	A	C	R	W	I	C	L	I	F
Q	U	Y	Q	Y	N	C	N	J	I	I	T	B	G	N
U	N	M	C	B	D	K	O	Q	R	P	R	C	K	I
H	N	W	P	R	Y	O	Z	T	L	O	M	K	H	L
Q	T	F	Z	K	H	L	Y	S	O	U	L	A	X	B
O	F	F	P	S	I	A	F	M	M	S	R	V	V	O
L	O	A	E	I	T	N	S	M	B	G	M	Y	S	G
G	O	V	M	M	M	T	P	K	Z	R	U	U	Y	R
R	V	A	B	W	I	E	O	A	D	Z	K	F	Q	G
N	J	Y	M	C	X	R	G	G	T	Q	D	N	W	X
J	A	G	K	O	H	N	Y	T	I	C	H	I	M	U
N	A	M	E	I	G	O	O	B	C	O	H	I	E	J
A	X	X	F	X	U	E	B	M	S	Q	G	P	W	D
H	H	O	Y	H	E	M	J	O	Z	F	C	Y	F	S

Page 165-166

1. Roses
2. None
3. Shears
4. Yes
5. Five
6. No
7. 21.0°C
8. A rake
9. A dog
10. No

Page 167

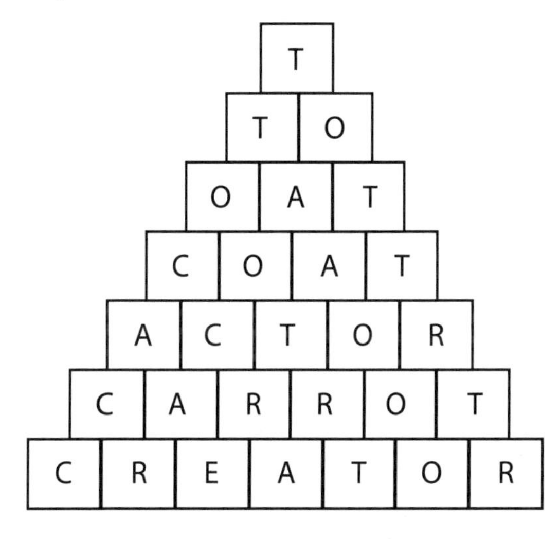

Page 168-169

Page 170

Answer: THEATRE

Page 172

Page 173

Page 174

Page 175

1. SAUCE
2. SCALE
3. SCENE
4. SCONE
5. SCORE
6. SENSE
7. SERVE
8. SHADE
9. SHAKE
10. SHARE
11. STORE
12. SHINE
13. SHORE
14. SKATE
15. SLATE

Page 176

B	U	E	Y	F	Z	P	Y	B	N	Q	M	G	E	N
B	O	U	N	D	A	R	Y	A	T	O	W	N	Q	K
H	W	W	N	T	T	C	Y	T	A	B	K	I	Z	I
E	I	N	L	R	G	Z	E	S	Z	E	T	D	Y	U
T	S	G	N	I	N	N	I	M	W	F	D	L	U	C
Y	E	L	C	U	N	S	R	A	O	I	G	E	C	E
K	G	K	I	H	P	G	G	N	H	O	Q	I	M	K
Q	T	K	C	P	Q	X	T	G	O	U	I	F	C	Z
H	W	A	U	I	U	A	C	G	D	B	J	I	H	I
K	N	M	G	R	W	E	B	A	C	O	R	E	P	Y
P	I	T	C	H	N	R	K	M	R	T	O	G	K	W
M	O	T	F	T	R	Q	T	S	T	S	F	F	X	L
Z	E	M	U	P	D	C	W	A	K	I	E	H	O	S
V	F	R	L	L	R	P	H	O	H	N	X	H	N	T
W	Y	U	Z	T	A	F	O	X	Z	C	V	R	K	E

Page 177-178

1. Yes
2. No
3. A bicycle
4. Yes
5. Yes
6. A toy car
7. Yes
8. Yes
9. 1234
10. No

Page 179

Page 180-181

Page 182

Answer: FRIENDSHIP

We hope you enjoyed our brain-tickling boredom bashing bonanza!